NOW IT IS KNOWN . . .

that there is not one schizophrenia but many,
each type of which appears to be caused by an
imbalance in body chemistry. This means that once
the source of trouble is located by accurate
diagnostic tests, such as HOD and EWI, there are
excellent chances of recovery through the use of
drugs, vitamins and other direct means of therapy
which may succeed where costly psychotherapy
fails.

Here is background information and advice from
professionals devoted to the diagnosis and treatment
of this family of diseases. They discuss schizophrenia
and autism in children, and give the reader a
wealth of useful knowledge including how
schizophrenics view their world; genius and
schizophrenia; sex and the schizophrenic; the
schizophrenic's relation to LSD, marijuana and
alcohol.

Here, for the first time in book form is sound,
sensible advice about

THE SCHIZOPHRENIAS: YOURS
AND MINE

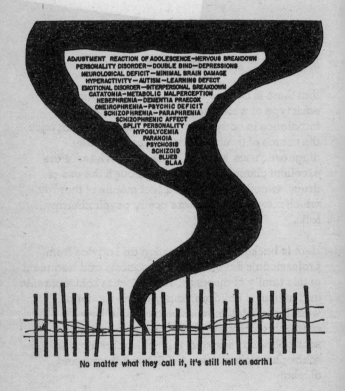

ADJUSTMENT REACTION OF ADOLESCENCE—NERVOUS BREAKDOWN
PERSONALITY DISORDER—DOUBLE BIND—DEPRESSIONS
NEUROLOGICAL DEFICIT—MINIMAL BRAIN DAMAGE
HYPERACTIVITY—AUTISM—LEARNING DEFECT
EMOTIONAL DISORDER—INTERPERSONAL BREAKDOWN
CATATONIA—METABOLIC MALPERCEPTION
HEBEPHRENIA—DEMENTIA PRAECOX
ONEIROPHRENIA—PSYCHIC DEFICIT
SCHIZOPHRENIA—PARAPHRENIA
SCHIZOPHRENIC AFFECT
SPLIT PERSONALITY
HYPOGLYCEMIA
PARANOIA
PSYCHOSIS
SCHIZOID
BLUES
BLAA

No matter what they call it, it's still hell on earth!

THE SCHIZOPHRENIAS
YOURS AND MINE

Prepared and Published by
The Professional Committee
of the Schizophrenia Foundation
of New Jersey

CARL C. PFEIFFER, Ph.D., M.D., *Chairman*

JACK WARD, M.D.

MONEIM EL-MELIGI, Ph.D.

ALLAN COTT, M.D.

A JOVE BOOK

The prime aim of The Schizophrenia Foundation of New Jersey is to make known how widespread this illness is, to tell people how vital it is to help eliminate suffering by recognizing its early symptoms and taking immediate action to control it and to point out how promising and worthy of support is the research now being devoted to it.

We must all learn that no one bears any blame for this illness and that it carries no stigma. Schizophrenics should be recognized during their illness as courageous people bravely battling one of the most dangerous and disabling of mankind's afflictions.

We want people everywhere to realize how much they can do to ease the burdens borne by those afflicted and by their families and to know the many ways in which as community members they can help in the recovery and restoration to normal life of those who have been stricken.

We urge the participation of all and we hope that this book will help to guide the way.

C. DAVID GREER
Chairman

The drawings on the front and back covers of this book are the work of Becca.

Eight previous printings
First Jove edition published October 1977

10 9 8 7 6 5 4 3 2

Printed in the United States of America

Jove books are published by Jove Publications, Inc., 200 Madison Avenue, New York, NY 10016

CONTENTS

FOREWORD

"For an illness which involves at least two million
casualties and their families in the United States alone,
and which is of enormous social and economic importance, public knowledge is extremely sketchy. Some
responsibility for this must lie with psychiatrists whose
voices have been confusing and whose opinions are
divided. There have been few comprehensible and con-
sistent attempts to inform and educate the sick, their
relatives, and society at large about the ravages which
this illness causes and what can and should be done
to reduce its enormous damage. Even the word "schizophrenia" has been allowed to become a matter for scorn,
stigma, and abuse, just as the words "plague" or "pox"
were used in the eighteenth century. Instead of protesting and enlightening the public with explanation
and education, psychiatrists have suggested feebly that
we should change the name of the illness to something
less frightening. A psychosis by any other name remains
one of the most appalling of human experiences and
is not in the least bit alleviated by being called a
"problem of living" or some other neutral statement,
which merely suggests that it is something lying beyond
the compass of medicine and, therefore, all the more
terrifying. Psychiatric timidity, sloth, and lack of enter-
prise combined with public fear, uncertainty, and ignor-
ance have been disastrous for patients and their families,
who are at the mercy of conflicting, dogmatic, and

often contradictory advice from a variety of experts of differing, and often, uncertain competence. Patients and their families often end by being completely confused, for these harrassed people are frequently able to obtain only meager information in spite of making diligent inquiries and search, often at great expense."

HUMPHRY OSMOND,
Journal of Schizophrenia,
Vol. 1, No. 1, 1967, p. 3.

**All the world is
queer
except me and thee and
sometimes I wonder about
thee!**

INTRODUCTION

THIS BOOK is offered to all people who have an interest in the schizophrenias; to the family who has a member presently afflicted; to the schizophrenic who is perplexed with disperception and now desires to do all in his power to keep well; to the many laymen, social workers, guidance counselors, teachers, members of the clergy, psychologists, and medical doctors who can help the patient to keep well and provide better diagnosis.

This primer was prepared as a public service by various members of The Schizophrenia Foundation of New Jersey. Realizing that no other illness known to man plays more havoc with life than the schizophrenias, we are compelled to publish. This book is probably the first of its kind for the public and is long overdue.

Our book includes suggestions for treatment, general information, and the results of literature review, tedious experiments, and studies by the writers. For years these dedicated scientists have done valuable research with medication, diet, and vitamins and now lean toward the biochemical approach for the control and eventual cure of the schizophrenias. The fact that the great majority of the patients are improving with rational therapy attests to the fact that this treatment seems to be the most effective to date.

Some of the information may seem quite technical to the layman, but this was included for the benefit of professional readers. Our aim is not to create a best seller, but to bring to a troubled and concerned audience what we hope will be constructive help.

Some may question a book that summarizes scientific data on the schizophrenias for the educated layman—particularly when some of the observations still need confirmation. We argue however that the press, magazines, and other news media are saturated with unproven opinions of lay and professonal therapists who still blame social interaction for all mental illnesses. A biologically oriented summary on schizophrenia will cause patients and their relatives to ask informed questions. These queries may cause more therapists to read medical literature and thus treat the schizophrenic more effectively.

A valid criticism of this book was given by one critic, who pointed out that the information is too scientific for the average patient and that the material should have been divided into two books—one for patients entitled, *Games Therapists Play*, the other for doctors entitled, *The Biology of Schizophrenia*. You, the lucky reader, now have two books for the price of one. If you don't understand one section, turn the pages until you find a meaty morsel you do understand!

NORMA RAUSCH, EDITOR

1. The Scope of the Schizophrenias

The schizophrenias lead both general diseases and mental disease as a cause of hospitalization. Since only one-third of the patients are hospitalized it is, indeed, the world's greatest disease.

In 1962, 712,174 or 51 per cent of the 1,406,818 patients who make up the daily hospital census were patients in psychiatric hospitals. This is slightly more than one out of every two hospital beds. There are more people in hospitals for mental illness than for all arthritis, cancer, heart disease, tuberculosis, and all other diseases combined. Ninety-eight per cent of all mental patients are in public hospitals, and only 2 per cent are in private hospitals. Diagnoses on patients with mental illness who were in a hospital in the United States are as follows for the year 1960:

Schizophrenia	23 %	
Alcoholism	14.6%	One-fourth are basically schizophrenic
Personality disorders	7.3%	Diagnosis?
Psychoneurotic reactions	6.9%	Diagnosis?
Mental deficiency	3.0%	
Epilepsy, Parkinsonism, etc.	13.9%	
Senility, brain damage, etc.	23 %	
Other psychotic disorders	8.3%	
	100 %	

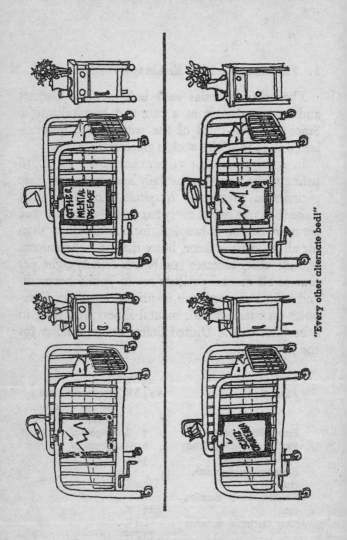

"Every other alternate bed!"

Because of the relative youth of schizophrenic patients and their low death rate, the hospitalized schizophrenics who are not discharged tend to accumulate from year to year and eventually make up half of the resident population of our public hospitals.

It is often repeated that heart disease is the number one killer. However, the nation's *main cause of hospitalization is schizophrenia,* which for the forgotten patient may mean a living death! These living deaths far exceed the actual deaths from any other disease. Yet the research effort in schizophrenia is minimal when compared to its massive morbidity. Voluntary contributions to heart diseases totaled 34 million in 1965, while the whole field of mental health collected only eight million of charitable dollars. The disproportion of these two donations is even more striking since more than one-third of the heart fund went into research efforts while only one-sixteenth of the mental health fund was spent in research.

Though limited as it is by the funds available, research on schizophrenia has made important breakthroughs in recent years, and many thousands of schizophrenics have already benefited greatly from these results. Beyond this, however, these pioneer studies have disclosed many other avenues which show much promise and should be promptly explored. Facilities and skilled personnel in most instances are available. Only financial support is lacking.

Among the many areas waiting to be studied, there are such practical projects as these:

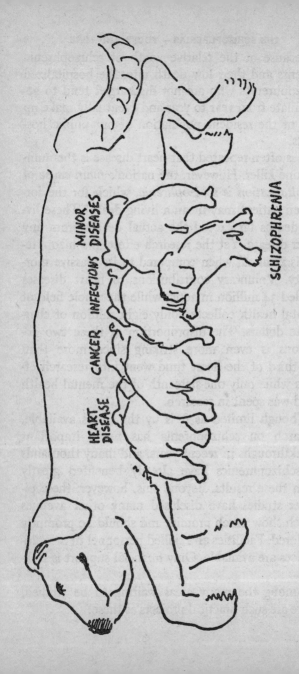

"Schizophrenia is the runt of the research litter."

1. Developing a series of sure-fire diagnostic tests for the presence of early schizophrenia: (a) psychometric, (b) brain waves and, (c) blood, skin, saliva, or urine tests are all needed. These tests must be made available to high school and college counselors.

2. Valid data on the effectiveness or lack of effect of megavitamin and other biochemical therapy.

3. Better understanding of the biochemical constitution of the schizophrenics. Are they hypoallergic? Are they auto-immune to their brains?

4. Careful study of the so-called schizophrenic families from the standpoint of their biochemical constitution.

5. What is the biochemical cause of the periodic schizophrenias? We should study those patients who are only ill a few days of the month or a few weeks of the year.

6. What are the biochemical and brain changes in postpartum psychosis? Hypothyroid psychosis?

7. What is the chemical or process that produces overstimulation of the brain in the schizophrenic?

8. How do the various antischizophrenic drugs work in the body?

For the sake of the hundreds of thousands of people whose lives are being blighted by this affliction and for the millions now living who otherwise will follow them, means must be found to advance this vital research. It is difficult to imagine any more worthwhile and promising utilization of the talents of our nation's skilled scientific personnel. Cancer usually hits life as it ebbs, while the schizophrenias cut down genius as it flows to fruition.

2. Neurosis or Psychosis

The old saying goes, "The neurotic builds castles in the clouds, the psychotic lives in these castles, and the psychiatrist collects the rent." A more appropriate punch line would be "and the psychiatrist issues the building permits," more appropriate since those who practice psychiatry are for the most part applying talking therapy, which is not effective in schizophrenia, but may be highly effective in some neuroses. Some types of talking therapy for mild schizophrenia will worsen the schizophrenia. A neurosis then is defined as a peculiar state of tension or irritability of the nervous system. A psychoneurosis is one of a group of minor diseases of the mind which are not actually psychoses. Examples of these are: abnormal anxieties, fears, and compulsions.

In contrast, a psychosis is defined as a serious disorder of the mind in which the patient is confused, lacks insight into his condition, and has a grave degree of disperception, depression, or hallucinations. If he knows that the hallucinations and disperceptions are not real then he has insight into his condition. If he believes in, or acts on the hallucinations, then he has *lost insight*. Examples are: the severe schizophrenias, manias and manic depression. Since Freud wrote, "The neuroses are, without exception, disturbances of the sexual function", many psychiatrists and psychoanalysts have adhered to this doctrine to such an extent as to warrant this comment by Robert Benchley, "The derivation of one color from the mixture of two other colors is not generally considered a sexual phenomenon, but that is because the psychoanalysts haven't got around to it yet."

The well-to-do patients who have neuroses, sexual problems, etc. are so numerous as to engage almost the full time of many of our best trained psychiatrists, so that little time is left for those patients who are more seriously ill both in and out of our hospitals. The psychoanalyst may take only one or two new patients each year, as he is so booked up with patients who continue in analysis year after year. If this therapy were effective in the schizophrenias the difficulty in using psychoanalysis for the treatment of one to three per cent of the total population would be immediately apparent. Yet another difficulty resides in the uneven distribution of talent. The great concentration of psychoanalysts is in our large cities whereas the seriously ill mental patients are usually sent to hospitals which are in rural areas where custodial care is cheaper, medical care inadequate and expert psychiatric care almost nonexistent.

The real problem in the treatment of the schizophrenias is the diagnosis and separation of the mild schizophrenias from the situational neuroses. This differentiation is very difficult if only a psychiatric interview is used. If, however, 1) past history, 2) psychometric tests and 3) responses to antianxiety and antipsychotic drugs are all known, then the differentiation can be accurately made. The neuroses respond to antianxiety drugs, while the mild schizophrenic states respond to antipsychotic drugs and megavitamin therapy. This therapeutic trial is frequently used by doctors to make a differentiation. Finally, the study of the disorder over a period of weeks and months will sometimes show that a chronic neurosis is really a mild schizophrenia. Dr. Calvin E. Schorer, in summarizing the data on admission diagnoses of the Lafayette Clinic in Detroit, found that of 344 patients initially diagnosed as schizophrenic only 31 or 9 per cent were later given a different final diagnosis. The average would have been higher except for the doctors' emotional reaction to the social implications of the behavioral and diagnostic label.

3. Genetics and Schizophrenic Families

The study of human genetics (the science of the inheritance of body characteristics and disease) has yielded real understanding of some diseases. We have learned that Queen Victoria was a mutant, so that her offspring inherited the sex-linked recessive gene which caused some of the males to be abnormal bleeders. An unusual triumph of biochemistry was the discovery that sickle cell anemia is caused by a combination of genes which results in a chemically abnormal form of blood pigment. The odds for occurrence of a few diseases can now be predicted with great accuracy. However, like all statistics, these apply to groups, but not to any individual or even family. For example, Huntington's chorea (Woody Guthrie's disease), a disease of the nervous system, is caused by a simple Mendelian dominant gene. This means the odds are one out of two that a child born to a carrier will develop the disease. The odds are the same for the sex of the child.

Many patients and their families are concerned about whether schizophrenia is inherited. Some families would be upset if it should be; others would be relieved. The upsetting part is the future appearance of schizophrenia in children and grand-children. The knowledge that the disease is heredi-tary would relieve the parents of their feelings of guilt springing from doubts about what they did wrong in rearing their child.

There have been many studies to try to learn whether schizophrenia is hereditary. The general consensus is that the schizophrenias, like diabetes, are inherited, but in a complex way.

For instance, we know that if one of a pair of identical twins has the illness, the probability is great (85 per cent) that the other will also, even if reared separately. For fraternal (nonidentical) twins or other brothers and sisters (siblings), the likeli-hood is not as great (only 14 per cent). Indeed, the incidence may be no greater than in other families. A basic difficulty with such studies is that schizo-phrenia is so widespread that, as with heart disease and cancer, no family escapes altogether.

Geneticists are puzzled as to the persistence in the race of any nondominant inheritance factor in schizophrenia, a disease which afflicts mankind be-fore full reproductive status is attained. The genet-icists postulate a beneficial factor which may help survival. In 1964, Sir Julian Huxley, Professor Ernst Mayr and Doctors Humphry Osmond and Abram Hoffer reported in *Nature* that schizophrenia persists in the human race because of a major dominant gene, SC, which has 25 per cent penetrance. The high incidence of schizophrenia (one or more per cent in general population) cannot be maintained by constant mutation alone. The reproductive fitness of the schizophrenic is only 70 per cent that of "normals," and suicide is frequent. Thus, the disorder should diminish except for certain advantages in life which accrue to the schizophrenic.

These eminent authors suggest that resistance to shock, histamine, abnormal endocrine function, and even to infectious disease may be the answer to the better survival of the schizophrenic. The Princeton group has provided some evidence for resistance to virus infections, in that schizophrenic children seldom have a head cold and are resistant to influenza in times of epidemic. Accurate data in regard to the viral infectious diseases of childhood would be most revealing. In addition to better survival, the female schizophrenic may be more fertile, but this remains to be determined. It will be of great importance to recognize carriers of the abnormal SC gene. This has been done by means of biochemical tests in other diseases.

4. Environmental Factors in Schizophrenia

Social stress is undoubtedly bad for the schizophrenic, but this is probably not the predominant cause of the disorder.

For the last 30 years in our culture, "Mother" has been made a scapegoat for many purposes. Among these was the concept of the *schizophrenic mother*. More recently, "*Father*" has been accused. This concept, that the parents are somehow responsible because their child develops schizophrenia, loses steam when it is realized that, typically, one child of a family grows up to be schizophrenic while all the brothers and sisters are normal. When a high family incidence of schizophrenia does occur, the usual rules of family interaction must be rewritten and each patient treated individually. Family studies of schizophrenics have reached great complexity, elaboration, and cost, yet they remain inconsistent and unconvincing.

Of course, families treat their schizophrenic members differently from others; they are different! Usually much discord is created by the patient's symptomatic acts. His emotional storms and, perhaps, threats, his ambivalence, negativism, and lack of perception provoke ambivalence or outright hostility from the others. Untreated schizophrenics may have no love for others in any mature sense and, correspondingly, may not themselves be lovable. The extent to which all this can be overridden by sympathetic understanding of the illness does have limits. Inescapable adverse emotional reactions are often a source of great distress to the family, especially to the mother who normally would have the tenderest feelings toward the patient. When she is continually rebuffed, ignored, and disconcerted by her untreated child, no good is done by insulting her further with accusations of blame for the problem, although patients themselves and even therapists often do so.

Much has been made over the newly hatched duck which promptly imprints in his brain the nearest object as a possible or surrogate mother.

Coming closer to man, much more has been made over the rhesus monkey reared with, or without, a mother. These are both harsh experiments with doubtful applicability to the human situation.

Any human baby who presently survives the first year of life has been fed, bathed, tidied, and loved to some extent. The schizophrenic child may show differences from his sibling's behavior as early as two months—with the same mother, who is not expecting grossly different responses from her new baby.

Another alternative is that the disease is somehow acquired after birth, but not merely as a psychological maladjustment. Little attention has been paid to this until recently, when the possibility that schizophrenia may be an auto-immune disease was raised by Dr. Robert Heath (see Biochemical Theories, Chapter 34). Another possibility for some schizophrenias might be viral infections of low pathogenicity as has been suspected in the leukemias. (See Biochemical Theories and Endocrine Factors, Chapters 33 and 34.)

At present, none of the foregoing alternatives stands out clearly. More work is needed badly. However, psychologically, the schizophrenias are a puzzle. In schizophrenia the family-environmental influence now seems very small. As a very exhaustive family study by Dr. Frances Cheek of the N.J. Neuropsychiatric Institute, recently concluded, the family reaction to the patient is more likely to be the *result* rather than the *cause* of his illness.

5. The Types of the Schizophrenias

The schizophrenias are decreasing. In 1900 they were X plus 7; now they are only X in number where X means "unknown." The separations were effected by finding the cause of other disorders which mimic schizophrenia perfectly. The seven separations are now called *dementia paralytica* (brain syphilis), pellagra (niacin deficiency), porphyria (abnormal form of chemical blood pigment,) homocysteinuria, thyroid deficiency, amphetamine psychosis, and Vitamin B-12-folic acid avitaminosis. Other specific entities will be separated from the hodgepodge we call the schizophrenias. Hence, we refer to the disorder in the plural as we do the epilepsies.

Yet another reason for speaking of the schizophrenias in the plural is the variation in their severity, duration, and symptoms. In the past, the serious schizophrenias have been labeled paranoid, simple, hebephrenic, catatonic, and mixed. These terms are of little help, since, except for the paranoids, the untreated patient may vary from month to month through all the diagnostic categories. The paranoid (unduly suspicious) usually stays true to his class and is the closest to normality in his quantitative brain waves, thoughts, and ideation. Simple therapy, such as adequate rest or quiet seclusion, can sometimes dispel the paranoia.

Some females have schizophrenia only at their menstrual or premenstrual period. Others have it only after the birth of a baby. One prolific housewife had a postpartum psychosis after the birth of her fifth, sixth, seventh, and eighth babies! Her only complaint was that her present doctor was trying to cure her with talking therapy instead of the shock therapy which had been previously very effective.

Schizophrenic patients usually should be told, when they ask about their illness: "Yes, you do have one of the schizophrenias, but this diagnosis, while real, covers disorders of extremely varying severity." Some patients have only mild disperception or thought disorder and go through life without treatment, handicapped, but not seriously impaired. Others have only feelings of unreality which may come in waves when they are overtired, and the condition never gets any worse and may decrease with the aging process. A few may have serious symptoms which can be completely controlled by thyroid therapy. Some have a complete remission with specific drug therapy, and, finally, some patients need every type of therapy that is now available. New research is constantly being done to improve antischizophrenic drugs, and our biochemical knowledge of the disorder is such that no one need any longer be afraid of the honest diagnosis of schizophrenia. As Dr. Nathan Kline has remarked, "We have better treatment for the schizophrenias than for the neuroses." Only by facing up to the extent of the disease will we control it, and research progress is such that another decade should disclose the cause and provide the cure.

An analogy to the schizophrenias can be drawn in the case of rheumatism (the arthritic disorders). Every adult over the age of 30 has some type of arthritis—usually osteoarthritis of a single joint,

"The best way I can explain it, Mr. Callahan, is to say, it's sort of a severe skin problem—with complications of course, but you don't have a thing to worry about."

such as a knee or the sacroiliac. Very few of us have rheumatoid arthritis in which multiple joints are hot and inflamed. In spite of the fact that arthritis can be a mild or a severe disease, the physician does not hesitate "to call a spade a spade" and tell the patient and close relatives that some type of arthritis exists. Effective treatments exist today for both arthritis and schizophrenia.

The recognition and treatment of schizophrenia has been held back by the failure of many physicians to realize its extent and by an unwarranted fear of schizophrenia. A patient recently remarked, "I am glad that I only have schizophrenia instead of a personality disorder. I know that schizophrenia responds to drugs, whereas any personality disorder would be hard to change."

Since the schizophrenias are not alike in outcome, but only in symptoms, the recognition of a schizophrenia is important so that early treatment and regular counseling can be started. Some schizophrenias are mild and will be controlled by a reduction in everyday stress. Some are more severe and may need megavitamin therapy. For serious symptoms one uses the effective antischizophrenic drugs, plus vitamins; and for the most severe, the patient may need electro-shock therapy (EST), plus drug and talking therapy. Remember the rule of Dr. James Blake (circa 1800): "One-third of the psychotics *recover spontaneously.*" Remember, too, that the *hospital discharge rate for even the severest form of the disease is a whopping 75 per cent.*

6. Differential Diagnosis of the Schizophrenias

The reader may well ask about the differential diagnosis of schizophrenia. We have already said that the schizophrenias were at one time much more numerous, namely X plus 7 similar disorders. Those seven syndromes, which were facsimiles of schizophrenia, are now separated from the schizophrenias. One may well ask if these disorders are still apt to be confused with schizophrenia. In regard to two, the answer is no; in regard to the last five, the answer is yes. In other words, the diagnostic tests for number one, namely brain syphilis, are now routine, and a blood serological test rules out the possibility of brain syphilis which might be confused with schizophrenia. The same is more or less true in regard to brain tumor. Brain tumors of the frontal lobe or of the mid-brain can be sometimes confused with schizophrenia; but the characteristic history, the presence of increased pressure of the spinal fluid and the frequent occurrence of convulsions, will usually eliminate brain tumor as a possible alternate diagnosis.

We then come to (number two) pellagra, which has almost disappeared, because many staple foods, such as corn meal and wheat flour, have niacin or niacinamide added in order to prevent pellagra when these foods are used as a main source of diet. Only in rare instances can an individual now get a dietary deficiency of niacin with a resultant pellagran psychosis. In other words, grave undernutrition is needed in order to produce this disease with present-day foods.

The diagnosis of porphyria (number three) is more difficult to eliminate, and, undoubtedly, some patients now labeled schizophrenic have had porphyria off and on during their lifetime. Fortunately, it is a rare disease, so the chance of a misdiagnosis is uncommon. Porphyria as a mental disease has been recently publicized by two British psychiatrists in the July, 1969, issue of the *Scientific American*. Drs. Ida MacAlpern and Richard Hunter point out that King George III of England, who was king of England at the time of the American Revolution, undoubtedly suffered from porphyria. At that time the cause of the disease was unknown, but he had the typical and classical symptoms of porphyria which are as follows: acute abdominal pain, which is followed by some constipation; darkening of the urine to a port wine color; weakness or even paralysis of the lower extremities; hoarseness; fast pulse, and convulsions. As the convulsions subside, the patient usually has a period of delirium, and the whole sequence of symptoms may come and go at yearly or ten-yearly intervals. In the case of King George III, these attacks were at ten-yearly intervals.

Drs. MacAlpern and Hunter point out that in 1941 one of our most prominent analytical psychiatrists, Professor Guttmacher, of Baltimore, reviewed the illness of George III from the angle of modern psychoanalysis. They state that, characteristic of the psychoanalytical viewpoint in cases of mental aberration, the analyst attaches little weight to physical symptoms and biological causes. Professor Guttmacher dismissed the king's physical complaints, attributing them in part to efforts by the Court to cover up the king's madness and, in part, to neurotic fabrications by the king himself. Describing the illness in modern times as manic-depressive psychosis, Dr. Guttmacher added that "self-blame, indecision, and frustration destroyed the sanity of George III, a vulnerable individual." He pictured the king as an unstable man, who could not tolerate his own timorous uncertainty, and broke under the strain. He suggested that had the king been a country squire he would in all probability not have had psychotic episodes. (Actually King George III was known to his subjects as "Farmer George" because of his interest in agriculture.)

This article on porphyria was considered of adequate newsworthy interest to be copied almost entirely by *The New York Times* in its issue of July 3, 1969. However, with kindness to the psychoanalytical school and its occasional misguided opinions about biological medicine, the author, Mr. Sullivan, omitted entirely the grave misdiagnosis of psychoanalyst Guttmacher. Mr. Sullivan, in addition to reporting on the family tree of the kings and queens of England from Mary, Queen of Scots, on down to the twentieth century, also adds several interesting details in regard to porphyria.

One is the fact that a colorless porphyria may appear which does not wave the usual red flag of port wine-colored urine. Thus the urine may appear normal; but the porphorin may result in photosensitization. In other words, the skin of the individual will be sensitive to sunlight.

Thyroid deficiency (number four) has been called myxedematous madness, because many patients who have inadequate secretion of the thyroid hormone will show the symptoms of schizophrenia. A slight degree of hypothyroidism may go unnoticed, and a few patients who seem to have normal thyroid function and schizophrenia will have their mental symptoms clear when thyroid is added to their therapeutic regime.

As for number five, we have discussed this in other parts of this primer. The use of weight-reducing tablets and the overuse of the amphetamine-type stimulant drugs can produce a syndrome which is indistinguishable from so-called schizophrenia. The patient may have paranoid schizophrenia or other classical types. This may happen to the unwary teen-ager or middle-aged woman who uses weight-reducing pills enthusiastically or even takes them exactingly as prescribed by an enthusiastic doctor. Thus weight reduction medications may precipitate schizoid symptoms, and the juvenile who has access to "speed," methedrine, or "Bennie pills" can induce abnormal ideation and behavior as a result of overstimulating his brain. A careful history is usually adequate to eliminate this type of drug-induced schizophrenia.

Yet another disease (number six) which may be confused with schizophrenia is homocysteinuria, which is one of the metabolic disorders in which the patient excretes the abnormal amino acid, homocysteine. This occurs in children and has been successfully treated by a low methionine diet plus additional pyridoxine, or vitamin B-6, in the diet. Under these circumstances the patient can usually grow normally without symptoms of mental disorder.

The most difficult diagnosis at present (number seven) is the differentiation of schizophrenia from vitamin B-12 and folic acid deficiency. The onset of vitamin B-12 deficiency can be insidious in the adult and will produce all of the symptoms of the paranoid or other types of schizophrenia.

The doctor must always keep this deficiency in mind when an adult patient develops symptoms of schizophrenia. Schizophrenia when it occurs for the first time in older adults is sometimes called "paraphrenia." Thus, the target organ for the vitamin deficiency may be the brain rather than the blood, and a patient may have a specific B-12-folate deficiency of the brain with only minimal anemia and, certainly, no signs of pernicious anemia. The importance of the early diagnosis of this deficiency is evident because we know that this type of disorder responds dramatically to B-12 and folate therapy and does not respond to the antipsychotic drugs. Thus the differential diagnosis of schizophrenia late in life presents many more subtleties and nuances than does the diagnosis of schizophrenia in the teen-age years when such a vitamin deficiency is not apt to occur.

Dr. E. H. Reynolds of The National Hospitals for Nervous Diseases, London, has been a pioneer in studying folate and vitamin B-12 levels of the blood of mental patients and epileptics. He has reported and others have confirmed that prolonged Dilantin use for antiepilepsy therapy will produce a specific folic acid deficiency. Thus a typical patient, who has had only grand mal seizures (epilepsy) during the early years of life, may develop by the age of 15 to 20 a folic acid deficiency and the full-blown symptoms of paranoid schizophrenia. This psychosis responds to the use of some other anticonvulsant, such as Valium, to control the seizures and the gentle use of small doses of folic acid and vitamin B-12 to raise the blood levels of these two vitamins and remove the deficiency.

Several patients at the New Jersey Neuropsychiatric Institute have been found who had a history of epilepsy of many years' duration and who had been treated vigorously with Dilantin to prevent the grand mal seizures. They then developed schizophrenia, and their blood samples showed their vitamin B-12 to be in the mid-range of normal and their folic acid levels to be one-half that of the minimal or lowest level ever encountered in normal people.

Obviously the old rule applies: "The doctor must think of the disorder in order to diagnose it." The difficulty in the accurate diagnosis of the schizophrenias, and mental disease in general, led Dr. Derek Richter, of England, to point out that, with present psychiatric diagnoses, one may be as accurate as children labeling dolls. One "Helen" is not another "Helen."

7. Schizophrenics Have Made and Can Make Notable Achievements

Alexander Pope's observation that "great wits near madness lie" was not original. Men have speculated since the earliest days on the dividing line between genius and madness. The results of these speculations have usually been confused and confusing. Some claim that genius, itself, implies the presence of schizophrenia, and others with equal dogmatism allege that all those who have any degree of schizophrenia become more stupid. The truth must be more complicated and dependent on the individual personality and profession. In all probability the artist can get by with more schizophrenia than the minister or teacher.

Many medical men, over the centuries, have commented upon the brilliance which is not infrequently, but by no means always, associated with early schizophrenia. Indeed, at one time it was popularly supposed that the overstrain of this brilliance had "induced brain fever" resulting in collapse of the mind. The late Dr. Alan Gregg, pointed out that the relatives were wrong when they said, "John overworked and had a nervous breakdown." One of the first signs of the disease is the ability to work day and night without adequate sleep.

Some years ago Dr. Joan Fitzherbert in England found, while treating children at a child guidance clinic, that in the period immediately preceding a psychotic "break" their intelligence increased measurably and greatly. During the illness, itself, their intelligence quotient (I.Q.) was not measurable; but as they became well, it returned to a lower level some 20 or more points below that shown in the period of prepsychotic brilliance. It seems not unreasonable to infer that here for a period, at any rate, the schizophrenia was enhancing the children's abilities. How might this occur? Modern biochemical theory suggests that these young schizophrenics add methyl groups to the brain amines, and this results in a continued druglike stimulation of the brain.

The great Thomas Willis, the neuroanatomist, writing in the seventeenth century, described the illness which we now call schizophrenia in these terms: "For these kinds of brains, like distorted looking glasses, do not rightly collect images of things nor truly display them to the rational soul." Since we now know that changes in perception of the world are an essential aspect of the schizophrenias, then it might seem probable that from time to time such changes would enhance certain abilities and that in some circumstances this enhancement, when coupled with an already intelligent mind, would result in something remarkably different. James Joyce, in the writing of his *Ulysses*, may possibly be an example of disperceptional brillance.

From about the years 1700 to 1900, our view of the universe was governed and largely limited by the formulations of the great Sir Isaac Newton, who combined the most extraordinary intuitiveness in physics with superb qualities as a mathematical technician. Sir Isaac was a remarkable man; he did much of his greatest work alone; he spent two years during the Black Death or plague in rather mysterious seclusion on the family farm in Woolstenhough in Norfolkshire doing, it seems, nothing. He had no books; there were no journals at the time; he did not correspond with anyone. At the age of 30 he became increasingly unwilling to undertake "natural philosophy," which we now call science, and his energies in subsequent years were devoted to an occult philosophy, Biblical interpretations, and governing of the mint to influence the financial policy of the country. Newton was abnormally suspicious, cantankerous, and in many ways very difficult. In his mid-fifties he had a clear-cut psychotic break that lasted for two years. The diarist, Samuel Pepys, a fellow member of the Royal Society, notes with satisfaction that "Sir Isaac is improving and no longer believes that we Fellows of the Royal Society wish to introduce royal duchesses to his bed." Sir Isaac's delusion seems to have been that plans were afoot to breed a race of supermen for whom he would be the involuntary father. He objected to this on the grounds that he had not been consulted. However, Sir Isaac did recover and lived to a very ripe old age.

Much more recently we have the great philosopher, Wittgenstein. He was a student of engineering and a philosopher and played a large part in the development of the branch of philosophy known as logical positivism, although he himself later abandoned it. Wittgenstein published very little indeed, and most of his writings have been collected by his students. Although his philosophical statements are like strange and obscure riddles, there is no question that his contribution to philosophical thinking is brilliant. His behavior, however, was very erratic. He disappeared for some years and was finally found working as a schoolteacher in the Austrian Alps. He was then coaxed back to Cambridge. During World War II he became an orderly at Guys Hospital in London. He had a curious habit of sitting for hours in the front row of a theater, looking at any film that happened to be running; he claimed that this would help to clear his thinking!

There is no doubt at all that Nijinsky, probably

the greatest dancer who ever lived, was a victim of
schizophrenia. We have a long account of his illness
by his wife, Romela. He eventually died in a hospital suffering from schizophrenia. Nijinsky's dancing, it is said, had an eerie quality. Some people felt
that he defied the laws of gravity. He, himself, explained this by saying that he got outside himself,
watched himself dancing, and so controlled his
movements. This was thought by many to be a fig-
urative statement. The evidence is, however, that
that was how Nijinsky experienced it; his efforts to
get other dancers to emulate him in this respect do
not seem to have been too successful.

Franz Kafka, the great Czech author, who wrote
those magnificent books, *The Castle* and *The Trial*,
and that strange story "Metamorphosis," was,
according to Rudolf Altschule, undoubtedly schizophrenic. He also suffered from tuberculosis. His nov-
els foreshadowed, in an extraordinary and horrible
preview, the Nazi regime and ultimately an author-
itarian world. There are also vivid and horrible ac-
counts of some of his schizophrenic experiences.
Perhaps his most appalling story is "Metamorphosis," in which the writer turns into some kind of
bug. This is described with such complete convic-
tion that one feels the author is giving an account
of something that happened to him. This is by no
means impossible, for many schizophrenic people
have extraordinary changes in the perceptions of
their body which cause them the greatest distress.
There is an interesting story from Janoush, Kafka's
friend, about walking down a street when a little dog
ran out of a doorway. Franz shied away and pushed
Janoush back as if a lion were coming at them.

Janoush said, "Don't worry, Franz, it's only a little dog." Kafka replied, "Some people would say it was only a little dog." Many schizophrenic people suffer from the experience that people and objects coming toward them get larger instead of seeming to come closer. This is called the breakdown of size constancy, and this little story of Janoush's illustrates it perfectly. As the dog moved closer towards him, it appeared to get much larger and so less like a dog and more like a lion! No wonder Kafka shied away.

William Blake is generally held by critics to be among those few who made the apex of English poetry. He is also regarded as one of the finest artists of all times, his tiny paintings today being worth hundreds of dollars per square inch. His books of poems, which he illustrated and printed himself by a special process, are worth their weight in gold many times over. To his contemporaries, however, he was regarded as completely mad. He spoke of God, the Father, talking to him personally and claimed he had seen his brother's ghost mounting to Heaven. He described one of his paintings as the ghost of a flea, which he had seen. He catalogued all of his paintings and announced that he was among the greatest of poets and painters. This was considered patently absurd at the time and merely the raving of a madman. That history has vindicated his self-estimate does not alter the fact that he may well have suffered from schizophrenia.

There are many others who have had or been suspected of having this grave illness. Some have made great contributions for good, others have been less beneficial. There are, at least, strong suggestions that Adolf Hitler's extraordinary visions of "The

Thousand Year *Reich*" may have been derived from a schizophrenic illness as a young man, and this may have been the basis of his paranoia, which caused his rabid and appallingly destructive anti-Semitism.

Van Gogh's pictures and life strongly suggest that he had schizophrenia, although there is considerable disagreement and discussion about this. The breakdown of the perceptual field is extremely suggestive.

In Arthur Miller's *After the Fall* there is an upsetting and beautiful account of Marilyn Monroe's steadily developing illness: It is, of course, known that her mother was ill for many years in a mental hospital. Although Miller never mentions schizophrenia, it seems at least possible that Marilyn's elusive charm and innocence sprang from those misperceptions which we know do occur with schizophrenia.

These examples of great schizophrenics should not be interpreted to mean, of course, that all those with schizophrenia are necessarily geniuses or artists. They do suggest that talented people have been able to make use of their illness in a remarkable and, sometimes, highly constructive way. Thus, the illness should not be seen as being purely negative. It should be recognized for what it is, part of the human condition, and therefore, worthy of our sympathetic understanding, study, and encouragement.

8. Psychometric Tests for the Diagnosis of Schizophrenia

Psychological tests can be helpful first in making the diagnosis as well as in following the progress of the patient. Tests can be roughly separated into three kinds, intelligence tests, personality tests, and diagnostic tests. Some tests combine the two functions of personality assessment and the diagnosis of psychological abnormalities.

Some of the more objective of these tests are designed to measure more or less specific types of mental activity such as: intelligence, achievement, vocational interests, or aptitude. Except for intelligence tests and the HOD or EWI test, these tests have little relevance to schizophrenia. Intelligence tests can be used not only to gauge over-all intelligence in comparison with other people's but also to determine whether a person is making fullest use of his capabilities. If the person shows some impairment in intellectual functioning, the intelligence test can help pinpoint the specific areas of difficulty. Patients with specific kinds of mental illness suffer from disabilities in different sorts of mental activity. For instance, persons with brain damage may be unable to deal with abstract and symbolic problems, while schizophrenics can manipulate these symbols, but often do so in unusual ways. Both schizophrenics and brain-damaged patients have trouble with some kinds of visual-motor tasks, but the troubles they have are so different as to be diagnostic. The intelligence test can also pinpoint family difficulties. Thus, a child with a subnormal

I.Q. of 80 will have trouble when the rest of the family are up in the genius range of I.Q., or 140.

The most widely used diagnostic tests are either projective or self-rating objective inventories. Projective tests consist of a series of more or less structured stimuli such as inkblots or pictures. There are no definitely right or wrong solutions, and the results consist of the patient's own perceptions, thoughts, and feelings that he has put into (projected into) the test material. There are many kinds of such tests with many ingenious means of drawing out expressions of the patient's inner mental machinery. Some are more or less explicit and have the advantage that scoring is on a reliable numerical scale and that a statistically reliable comparative basis is possible. The disadvantage is that the leeway afforded to the patient to put things in his own way is limited. Tests in which the problem material is less explicit give the patient more room for diverse responses, but become correspondingly harder to score on a quantitative or numerical basis. The choice of tests, as well as the complex sifting and weighing of results is the work of highly trained personnel, usually clinical psychologists who are specially trained in projective techniques.

To a trained person, there is seldom much difficulty in deciding from a well-selected group of tests whether a patient has one of the schizophrenias. Indeed, even to an experienced clinician the change in the records of these patients from the original tests are sometimes surprising. This occurs when the patient is in a state of spontaneous remission or, for instance, when he is well-managed with modern medication. The tests also show surprising differences—sometimes between actual behavior and test results. This type of patient is sometimes hanging on to reality by sheer willpower.

A recent noteworthy development is the availability from the Roche Institute of a service, in which a complicated test, the Minnesota Multiphasic Personality Inventory (MMPI), is scored and interpreted by a programed computer. This is very complete in scoring all possible factors. The evaluation of the report is still up to the physician, since even this test is not infallible.

Precise detailing of the test findings in schizophrenia would be lengthy, complicated, and outside the scope of this book. In general, though, the disease causes a *loss* of adaptive ability. The patient cannot deal effectively with various kinds of mental tasks except insofar as they happen to coincide with one or another of the vagaries produced by the disease. Otherwise, his functioning is haphazard, maladaptive, and often completely out of step with reality. When the patient is better, this disperception diminishes; as he gets worse, the variation grows, and normal thought, feeling, and perception slip away. Only a chaotic shambles of disperception remains, and the patient is depressed about the situation.

Recently two simple questionnaire tests have been used to test improvement in the patient's state of disperception and schizophrenia. One is the HOD card-sort test of Drs. Abram Hoffer and Humphry Osmond, and the other is the EWI test. The HOD card-sort test is the Hoffer-Osmond Diagnostic Test. The EWI is the Experiential World Inventory test as developed by Dr. M. El-Meligi and Dr. Osmond at the New Jersey Neuropsychiatric Institute, Princeton.

Both tests give numerical ratings for nine different abnormalities of behavior which are most helpful in judging the patient's degree of illness and progress with therapy. The tests also disclose suicidal or homicidal tendencies. Several enterprising high school counselors have used these tests to ascertain the type and degree of illness of teenagers.

The use of the HOD and EWI tests will make it possible to correlate by a scientific method the biochemical imbalance and psychological disorders of the schizophrenias and eliminate to a great extent the usual diagnostic guesswork.

9. Who Should the Patient See First?

Quick thinking is needed and handy references must be used when the acute schizophrenic appears at the emergency room of a general hospital either with an overdose of some drug or perhaps in need of rapid and effective tranquilization.

With chronic schizophrenia or mild symptoms, the family can be more selective in regard to the choice of a physician. The physician to be consulted can be a well-trained general practitioner, neurologist, internist, or a biological psychiatrist. Any one of these physicians is capable of diagnosis and the direction of treatment. These physicians will probably order psychometric or other tests if these are needed to establish the diagnosis. If time is available the family can get sound advice from local or state chapters of the Schizophrenia Foundation.

The addresses of some of the Schizophrenia Foundations are:

American Schizophrenia Foundation
305 South State Street
Ann Arbor, Michigan 48108
(313) 761-8592

Schizophrenia Foundation of New Jersey
Box 25
Skillman, New Jersey 08558
(609) 466-2445

Schizophrenia Foundation of New York
National Arts Club
15 Gramercy Park
New York, New York 10003
(212) 754-1194

Schizophrenia Foundation of Connecticut
6 Longview Drive
Bloomfield, Connecticut 06002
(203) 242-8067

Schizophrenia Foundation of Greater
    Washington
12 Hilltop Road
Silver Spring, Maryland 20910
(301) 589-9348

Schizophrenia Foundation of California
30 Yorkshire Drive
Oakland, California 94618

Los Angeles Bay Chapter
15127 Sutton Street
Sherman Oaks, California 91403

Southern California Chapter
33915 Del Obispo Road
Dana Point, California 92629

Napa Valley Chapter
2261 Adrain Street
Napa, California 94558

North California Bay Chapter
84 Las Juntas Way
Walnut Creek, California 94596

Orange County Chapter
8596 Jennrich Avenue
Westminster, California 92863

Schizophrenia Foundation of Illinois
Lock Box 1088
Chicago, Illinois 60690

Central Illinois Chapter
203-B Senior Officers Row
Chanute Air Force Base
Rantoul, Illinois 61866

Minneapolis Chapter
American Schizophrenia Foundation
3715 West 22nd Street
Minneapolis, Minnesota
(612) 330-4612

Schizophrenia Foundation of Missouri
P. O. Box 207
Valley Park, Missouri 63088

Schizophrenia Foundation of Michigan
Box 406
Ann Arbor, Michigan 48107

Schizophrenia Foundation of Ohio
6028 Mayfield Road
Suite 9
Mayfield Heights, Ohio 44124

Schizophrenia Foundation of Rhode Island
1478 Atwood Avenue
Johnston, Rhode Island 02919

Schizophrenia Foundation of Westchester
28 Coutant Drive
New Rochelle, New York 10804

Schizophrenia Foundation of Georgia
2639 Peyton Road, N. W.
Atlanta, Georgia 30318

Schizophrenia Foundation of Maine
Guilford
Maine 04443

Schizophrenia Foundation of Maryland
16115 Oak Hill Road
Silver Spring, Maryland 20904

Schizophrenia Foundation of Massachusetts
11 Jacqueline Road, Apt. E
Waltham, Massachusetts 02154

Jefferson City Chapter
1940 Allen Drive
Jefferson City, Missouri 65101

Schizophrenia Foundation of North
    Carolina
P. O. Box 237
Bryson City, North Carolina 28713

Schizophrenia Foundation of North Dakota
Drayton
North Dakota 58225

Schizophrenia Foundation of Oregon
477 E. 32nd Street
Eugene, Oregon 97405

Schizophrenia Foundation of Vermont
95 Caroline Street
Burlington, Vermont 05401

Schizophrenia Foundation of Virginia
311 Hummingbird Road
Richmond, Virginia 23227

Schizophrenia Foundation of Saskatchewan
800 Spadine Crescent East
Saskatoon, Sask., Canada
(306) 527-7969

Canadian Schizophrenia Foundation
347 Bay Street
Toronto 1, Ontario, Canada

Schizophrenia Foundation of British
Columbia
Hollywood Hospital
New Westminster, B. C., Canada

Bolivia Schizophrenia Foundation
Casilla 370
Cochabamba, Bolivia, S. A.

List here the addresses and phone numbers of the Schizophrenic Foundation and other mental health clinics in your area:

10. Is Something Wrong with my Mind or Senses?

Probably there is no more horrifying speculation, doubt, or fear! For man's senses, mental function, and, particularly, his memories are his identity. If he cannot remember his past and if he cannot deal with his present in terms of his past, then in a very real way as an individual he does not exist. Anything which tends to interfere with normal brain function is a dire threat, indeed.

Several main types of natural psychotic illness occur which cause a person to feel that something may be wrong with his mind. The schizophrenias is the class that is the most severe, the most widespread, and the greatest cause of hospitalization. Even when used in the plural the term *schizophrenias* is an inadequate and misleading one.

There are many conflicting descriptions and explanations for the schizophrenias, but at a basic level, there is usually little difficulty in making a diagnosis; and there is usually agreement among physicians in making the diagnosis, even though they may disagree about the causes and ulimate outcome of a given case. Since the schizophrenias may vary in severity from simple (but abnormal) feelings of disperception or persecution to complete loss of contact with reality, the physician hesitates to apply the term *schizophrenia* to the mild forms of the disorder. Instead he uses schizoid personality, schizophrenic reaction, or other unsuitable words. The doctor really means: "I am puzzled and will ride the fence until I see what happens to you in the next year or so as you free-wheel with or without medication."

Uniform features of the schizophrenias, on which doctors agree, are that they are disorders of thought, perception, and experiencing or interaction. The schizophrenias are a subjective or personal malady, with no clear or reliable external manifestations, which can be seen in a neurological disease. A maimed leg, however painful and disfiguring, would

"Let's see if scotch-tape works!"

be easier to bear, because it is objective and obviously real. The lack of firm, objective signs is perhaps the crux of the continuing argument as to whether the schizophrenias may have any physiological or biochemical basis. This will be reviewed later in more detail.

Some of the schizophrenias can be likened to a nightmare state from which there is no certain awakening. Even more accurately, the experiences of schizophrenics are reproduced in certain toxic or febrile states. The normal person on recovery from a high fever with delusions, can breathe a great sigh of relief at the thought that his experience was temporary and will not recur until the next high fever. The person under LSD has the clock as his best friend, since this drug-induced schizophrenia will wear off with time. For the person with schizophrenia, however, the problem is a continuing nightmare.

When is it an illness? A just point of debate is whether certain kinds of mental derangement actually qualify as illnesses. With most clearly organic illnesses, there is no difficulty. For example, if a patient has a case of pneumococcal pneumonia, there is no question. Objective signs, such as fever, are present, and the invading bacterium can be found. Similarly, patients who have certain mental symptoms after strokes or infections of the brain present no problem in being considered ill. In contrast, there is a group of disorders listed, in the standard nomenclature of the American Psychiatric Association, as "character and behavior disorders." There is nothing in these terms to suggest any organic or physiological derangement, so that to call them illness, although currently fashionable, is stretching the term considerably.

Intermediate between these extremes are patients with the two major psychoses, the schizophrenias and manic-depressive psychosis. It has become popular also to regard manic-depressive psychosis as "better" than schizophrenia. Manic-depressive psychosis has long been felt by some psychiatrists to have an organic basis, and anyway, they claim it "is only a disorder of emotions, the patient isn't really crazy." Perhaps this is in part because intellectual functioning may be less impaired than in severe schizophrenia. The latter has become something of a dirty word, a diagnosis to be whispered and, often, to be concealed from patient, family, or friends. Again a maimed leg or even blindness would be more bearable, because it is visible, explicable, and being plainly physical, is something one need not be ashamed of.

Socially determined bias plays its part also in the way in which the two kinds of major psychoses are regarded. In a way, to be depressed fits in with an ideal of tragic nobility and with Puritan morality. "To be good, you must suffer," while to be schizophrenic often means to be disorderly, disruptive, and, at times, downright disgusting. Other illnesses also are dismaying sometimes, such as chronic tuberculosis; but here again, there is a tangible organic basis to excuse the patient and the disease.

Yet schizophrenia, about which some people have such strong and irrational feelings (no doubt because of their own fears or other emotional reactions), strikes everywhere throughout all of mankind. The commonly quoted figure of one per cent of all humanity is probably far short of the actual incidence. We should add the "walking wounded," who are never seen by any physician, since only one-third of those afflicted need to be hospitalized. We must also add the teen-ager who commits suicide before a diagnosis is made! Thus, the problem is one which is important from the viewpoint of numbers, as well as individual misery. Heart disease may cause more deaths, but the schizophrenias cause more heartache. Given a choice, most of us who have tasted adult freedom would prefer quick death to the aimless custody of many mental institutions, which usually is the fate of the *untreated* schizophrenic!

What brings the patient and the doctor together? The things which characterize untreated schizophrenia can be separated into two classes: those which bother the patient and those which bother others around the patient. The two may not be the same. In fact, there is often considerable friction between the patient and others. Consider the case of a man who says he has visions and hears the voice of Jesus. Hallucinations are considered by doctors to be evidence of psychosis; but this man is a lay preacher of the church which teaches that if you only have enough faith, Christ will appear in person! To him then, the people who say he is mentally ill are merely a bunch of nonbelievers. This preacher is an example of the fact that leadership and secondary gain frequently go with the delusional-hallucinatory system of many paranoids. Many of the stresses and frustrations of everyday life could be assuaged if one had a firm belief in being chosen men of God (many people have this without being delusional about it, of course). A paranoid can get a great deal of authority and excitement out of his distorted belief about the FBI, communists, and the tax collector.

This discord creates certain practical difficulties. Consider the case of a paranoid young woman. She keeps insisting to her family that there is a mysterious man who has a plot to seduce her and make her a white slave. Lacking evidence to support this, the family is upset and annoyed by her continued delusions, as well as by her untidiness, uncooperativeness, and unpleasantness around the house. Complaints then are made to the family physician by the family, not by the patient. The patient refuses flatly even to talk to the physician, insisting that she is in good health. "It's just that her family doesn't understand and isn't sympathetic." This kind of situation can create a dilemma for the physician. Although the diagnosis is reasonably clear, should he insist on treating a patient who has not asked for his services? Of course, if the patient asks for help there is no problem. If the patient presents some clear evidence that he (or she) may harm someone, intervention is clearly justified; but aside from the unethical taint of unsolicited treatment, a major goal is to keep patients out of the hospitals whenever possible. Sometimes that alone is a victory, because, with some of our present mental hospitals, there is a probability that the patient may be better off at home. One situation which creates great difficulty occurs when the physician suspects that the patient *may* become suicidal or homicidal. Since the conservation of human life has high priority, the physician must hospitalize the patient. Being only human and acting on the basis of insufficient tests, the doctor is sometimes wrong, no matter how great his ability. Patients, after such a false alarm, are often bitter and unforgiving. Indeed, they frequently incorporate the memory of such an episode into their delusional systems.

"A perverse, ungrateful, maleficent malady . . . ," might be aptly applied to schizophrenia. Since the disease is effectively destroying the useful life of the patient during the very years when he should be at fullest physical and mental productivity, he, therefore, seems to others perverse, ungrateful, and maleficent. The mental quirks which schizophrenia may elicit most uniformly are guaranteed to destroy the patient's close relationships with others and to set them against him. This is mitigated only if other people are sufficiently understanding to realize that these are disease symptoms and discount them. These symptoms are given in the section describing the illness in detail, but the point to be made here is how effective these are in destroying the relationships of the patient to others. The symptoms fall into two groups, those which alter the feelings of the patient about others and those which alter the feelings of others about the patient. In the first group, irrational fear may readily turn to suspicion, hostility, or hate. The patient is in the grip of extreme ambivalence, so that even those whom he really loves may becomes objects of hate and fear. No one can be trusted; no one can be loved, everyone must be doubted. Hence the patient may be effectively cut off from a warm relationship, even from those from whom he might derive solace, if not actual beneficial support, in the midst of his affliction. Concurrently, this may lead him to behave as if deliberately alienating his loved ones. Besides treating them with hate, he also is likely to manifest negativism, so that everything which might act to correct the deteriorating situation becomes fuel to feed the fires. Thus, the patient may become ever more isolated on his own desert island in a sea of loneliness, fear, and hate, and too often his family becomes ever more willing to leave him that way because he rebuffs their every attempt to help.

11. My Schizophrenia Is Like This— The Patient Speaks

1. "When I am ill I lose the sense of where I am. I feel 'I' can sit in a chair, and yet my body is hurtling out and somersaulting about three feet in front of me."—Catherine

2. "Cars *seem* to be much closer than I know they really are, so driving is difficult."—Bob

3. "When I feel illest, down in a dark pit, all alone, I wish someone would reach out and take my hand—to remind me where 'I' begin, but something else (perhaps my sickness) keeps me from asking. I both want people to touch me and help me, yet I am afraid when they do. At these times I have no voice—I feel utterly alone."—Jane

4. "It is really very hard to keep up conversations with others because I can't be sure if others are really talking or not and if I am really talking back."—Judith

5. "I don't want to write anything about my illness for the book. It's all still too fresh in my mind. To remember enough to write it down would be to go back into hell again. I'm not strong enough to do that yet."—Beth

6. "I feel like a female Dr. Jekyll and Mr. Hyde—I never know in the morning what person I'll be when I get up."—Mary

7. "I used to think it was groovy to be 'high' all the time until my 'lows' went so low I couldn't climb out. Now I've learned to give up the 'top of the highs' so that my 'lows don't have to hit bottom

either. It's a matter of a delicate balance, and I guess now I'm a real 'square'."—Paul

8. "The worst part of my illness is when time slows down and 'the door to the future' is closed. You wake up one morning, and suddenly 'there's no tomorrow'; you can't say to yourself 'I'll feel better tomorrow if I can get through today, because the next day doesn't exist. As soon as I can see that to-morrow will really come, then time goes back to normal, and I feel better."—Richard

9. "A hospital is no place to ask for help! At three o'clock in the morning when you are dying and the morning's never coming, they say 'go back to bed, dear, your doctor will see you in the morn-ing.' When you feel just great they load you up with Thorazine, and then you can't move or think or anything."—Jimmy

10. "When ill, I suffer from severe hallucinations and the physical presence of much-felt ghosts within my body. I feel I am possessed to a very uncom-fortable degree. I have spells of extreme discomfi-ture, usually in the evenings, which last for as long as six or seven hours, in which I am forced to lie down and sweat it out in extreme fear and dis-comfort. I can hardly restrain myself because of the violent and teasing movements of the spirits in the locality of my buttocks and pelvis. During this frightening period, I sweat a lot and have difficulty breathing. I also have tightening of the chest when the spirits encroach upon me there. I hear these ghosts, as well as see them. Their acute presence is felt every minute of my unhappy existence, and I am in a state of misery at all times because of them."
—Edward

11. "Purple Shadows flow beneath my tears
and Silently I watch
The river of life
flow past my soul
Leaving me a silent
Stranger to all."—Jean

12. Danger Signs of the Schizophrenias

1. Stereotyped or repetitive behavior.
2. Continued feelings of physical discomfort without cause.
3. Unnatural fears or unnatural grandiosity.
4. Failure to make friends and unnatural ability to alienate loved ones.
5. Unfounded suspicions or threats.
6. Profound insomnia, i.e., the ability of a teen-ager to work or carouse all night.
7. Profound daytime fatigue or stuporlike sleep (he may go to bed when he comes home from school).
8. Continued angry excitement or temper tantrums in a teen-ager.
9. Complaints that voices are too loud or all lights are too bright.
10. Hallucinations
    (a) Hearing voices unnaturally.
    (b) Seeing visions unnaturally.
    (c) Smelling bad odors without cause.
    (d) Unnatural abilities: "I read others' thoughts," "They read my mind."
11. Talk of suicide.
12. Announced sudden belief in the great truth phenomena, such as:

    (a) "God is Love."

    (b) "Love is the only thing that matters."

    (c) "I didn't ask to be born."

    (d) "My basic problems must be solved."

Note well: Single symptoms are not diagnostic; several of these signs must be present.

13. Is the Schizophrenic Dangerous?

When the young student from Texas climbed the campus bell tower, with rifle in hand, and shot down innocent bystanders, the press and even talking therapists cried:"Beware! Schizophrenia!" Although the autopsy ultimately showed a mid-brain tumor as the probable cause of this antisocial act, the damage had been done. The public cringes at the thought or sight of a poor unfortunate who doesn't talk sense. Of all the schizophrenics, only the suspicious or paranoid patient is dangerous, and he represents only a small and usually stable fraction of the schizophrenias. Unlike a patient with a growing brain tumor, who may explode into violence unforeseeably, a paranoid develops slowly and usually gives many signs of his illness before acting on his suspicions. Of course, these signs should not be ignored. This points up once again the importance of early diagnosis and treatment. Once classified, the paranoid usually stays that way—just overly suspicious, vocal, and extremely slow to back his words with action. If he can live an isolated life, with minimal social contacts, he can at most times be productive and respected. When pushed or ridiculed he may break under the stress, so he must be watched carefully!

In addition to patients with brain tumors, the patient in the manic stage of manic-depressive disorder can be destructive and assaultive. By far the greatest danger of assault arises from the individual with a character disorder who deliberately plans a violent career to meet his needs in life.

One psychiatrist has repeatedly said that if he were looking for a safe neighborhood to live in, he would choose one that was entirely schizophrenic, because the possibilities of violence in such a neighborhood would be a great deal less than that in the average neighborhood.

Most untreated schizophrenics are meek, withdrawn, and occupied with their own thoughts or delusions. If they hear voices, the voices may even be heavenly or exalting. Only rarely do the voices suggest violence, and then many patients will tell their friends or doctor what the voices are suggesting. Again we are forewarned, and in the overwhelming majority of cases the schizophrenic does successfully battle with his negative voices if he has any. Under antipsychotic medication the patients come to doubt the voices or other hallucinations, so that while they may hear them, they don't believe them.

With appropriate therapy, the patient can be taught to recognize hallucinatory voices as opposed to real ones. For instance, such a simple thing as the question: "Can you talk to those voices without opening your mouth?" will help the individual differentiate between the real and the false.

Finally, although remembered, the hallucinations disappear, and the patient may refer to them only as those silly voices that he used to hear; or preferably, the individual may be able to realize that the "silly voices" were or are hallucinations which are an expression of his schizophrenia and, as such, are to be disregarded as a basis for action in his life.

"Possibly you tend to over-complicate things, Mr. Callahan?"

Since we are dealing with your schizophrenias and mine we should not close this topic without some mention of the hyperideational paranoid. He may be the executive in high places who has many ideas—in fact, *too many* so that he himself gets little or nothing done. If he has understanding and controlling colleagues he may be of value to the organization. If, however, he has absolute control of the business he can soon send it into bankruptcy. Such an individual was Adolf Hitler, whose havoc and infamy will live forever in history. With this horrible example of the hyperideational paranoid in mind, many organizations get psychometric tests on candidates for executive positions. Obviously these individuals can be used for their free flow of ideas but should not be depended on for logical administration.

14. The Very Real Risk of Suicide

The rising suicide rate among students is alarming. Suicide by students now ranks third as a cause of death in the 15- to 19-year age group. Suicide ranks second as the cause of death among college students. No greater tragedy can befall a family or the family doctor than to learn that a brilliant student has decided he's "had it" and takes final, successful action. The high incidence of suicide at this age period coincides with that period in life when the onset of schizophrenia is at its highest incidence. Suicide in schizophrenics is 20 times more prevalent than in the normal population. In general, homicide is grossly overrated and suicide among schizophrenics underestimated.

"Rest assured, Mr. Callahan, teen-agers are often subject to these little 'emotional disorders' but they soon grow out of them!"

Suicide is more commonly taken to be a hazard of a temporarily depressed mind rather than that of a serious mental illness, because the relationship of obvious sadness and the wish to "end it all" is readily understandable. Yet self-destructive impulses and actions are common in schizophrenia. For example, young persons with so-called "emotional instability reactions," for all their obvious aggressiveness and destructiveness toward other people, are often intensely *self-destructive* as well. The manifestations of destruction vary in form and intensity, ranging from minor self-mutilation to more or less serious attempts at suicide, sometimes in bizarre and grisly ways. Much of this emotional illness may be early schizophrenia. In the days before the advent of modern drug therapy it was not at all uncommon to see schizophrenic patients who had burned themselves with cigarettes or had cut themselves with shards of broken glass. These acts may have a symbolic quality. The patient may burn himself on the hands and feet so that the scars are an imitation of the wounds of Jesus. He may leap from a window, thinking that he has been transfigured and can fly. Thus these acts often arise from the patient's delusional thinking. In addition, however, schizophrenics may be severely depressed, and their self-injury may spring from this just as with other people who are depressed. There is a further hazard. In some patients certain drugs may intensify depression, so judicious tailoring of drug therapy for each patient is imperative. This takes time and patience on the part of both doctor and patient.

As stated above, suicide as a result of schizophrenia may occur much earlier in life than that from other causes. Suicides caused by depression occur late in life, in association with the menopause or hardening of the arteries of the brain. Thus, in still another way schizophrenia cuts down the young, and the total years of useful life that are lost are greater. Unfortunately, suicidal actions are sometimes among the very first evidences of the onset of the disease. Many a patient is already dead by the time the shocked and grieving family realizes in hindsight that something was, indeed, dreadfully amiss. This makes the need for early diagnosis (such as thorough screening in schools) and prompt, effective therapy all the more pressing.

The high suicide rate among young schizophrenics may seem surprising, and many people have viewed these suicides as impulsive, "crazy" incidents. However, in talking with young schizophrenics, one soon learns of their despair about their distorted world and their lack of hope of ever getting well. They are often told that they have nothing wrong with them except emotional instability, and the "authoritative therapist," who says "get hold of yourself and behave," brings no relief. Given an experience such as this, it really does not seem so strange that they commit suicide.

Most discussions of suicide rapidly turn into a detailing of statistics. However, statistics can be dehumanizing and to the family, friends, and physician, not to mention the patient, are irrelevant to the individual case. On this level, the statistics don't matter. The important thing is to save a human life whenever possible. If all present-day treatment has failed, at least, the patient can be preserved until the advent of better therapeutic measures. With these new treatments perhaps the suicidal cases may respond the best.

Talk or threats of suicide must always be taken seriously by both relatives and therapists. Patients will frequently give their real intent more openly in their answers to the psychometric tests, such as the EWI, HOD, or MMPI tests. In these tests a high dysphoria score, a low euphoria score, and a high impulsivity score show that the patient is actively suicidal.

Suicide prevention centers can help by referring the patient and his family to the appropriate treatment center. In New York City, two such centers are available.

Kings County Hospital Center,
Phone (212) 462-3322
National Save a Life League,
Phone (212) 687-2142

The Telephone Company is working on a national emergency service center which, when operative, will bring help by dialing 911.

Help is also available from your local chapter of Schizophrenics Anonymous. The address and phone number will be found in the yellow pages of the phone book.

Middlesex County has pioneered in the State of New Jersey in establishing a crisis phone with 24 hour service. This number is Liberty 9-6000 or 201-549-6000.

15. When to Hospitalize

The four clinical conditions in the schizophrenias which usually require hospitalization are: (1) When the patient attempts or threatens suicide, (2) When the patient is paranoid with agitation and threatens bodily injury to others, (3) When the patient's behavior interferes with the normal life of the family, (4) When the patient is uncooperative and will not take medicine of any kind, he usually must be hospitalized for initial treatment, and then can be given weekly injections of one of the long acting preparations.

Aside from these conditions most other schizophrenic states may be treated at home if the family will cooperate. The four instances for hospitalization listed above do not necessarily require state, county, or private psychiatric hospitalization. With proper medical supervision, the medical section of a general hospital can give effective and rapid treatment with a resultant rapid return of the patient to his home for continued treatment.

Home treatment may be better for many schizophrenics. This decision must be made by the physician in charge. A study of 152 state hospital patients by Dr. Benjamin Pasamanick in the Louisville, Kentucky, area provides some thought-provoking data. The patients were divided into three groups: 57 were given antischizophrenic drugs while living at home, 41 were given dummy capsules while living at home, and 54 as a control group were hospitalized for drug therapy. The two home-care groups were visited regularly by a public health nurse from the community mental health center. These visits were made weekly for the first three months, every two weeks for the next three months, and monthly thereafter for up to thirty months in some instances. The nurse renewed the patients' supply of drugs.

At the close of the study, 77 percent of the home-care patients were socially rehabilitated. Only 34 per cent of those on dummy capsules were able to stay at home. The hospital control group needed 83 days on the average for the social rehabilitation of their patients which meant that the 57 drug patients treated at home had saved almost 5,000 hospital-patient days.

According to the report, the hospitalized group required hospitalization more often after discharge than did the home-treated group. The numbers of readmissions are 25 out of 54 (46 per cent) for the hospital group and 13 out of 57 (23 per cent) for the home-treated group. Dr. Pasamanick suggests that early home drug treatment is the only type of prevention of schizophrenia presently available. One cannot easily humanize the hospital, but the dehumanizing effect of large institutions can be prevented by home treatment. Long term hospitalization increases the patients' withdrawal from society, makes them more dependent and less able to function normally.

Obviously, the family must be willing to have the patient stay at home and must be willing to tolerate the strange behavior of the patient before the anti-schizophrenic drugs start their good effect.

As a clinching argument, Dr. Werner M. Mendel recently reviewed the hospital records of 3,000 hospitalized schizophrenics and found that the discharge rate was 76 per cent, regardless of whether the patient had been hospitalized seven, 30, 60, or 90 days. The discharge rate of 76 per cent is thus independent of the number of days spent in the hospital.

Since many of our psychiatric hospitals, such as private and veterans' hospitals, have a waiting list for admission, the physician should not allow vigorous drug treatment to be delayed simply because a psychiatric bed is unavailable.

16. When the Patient Returns From the Hospital

1. The doctors' orders should be carefully followed (and this is extremely important).

   (a) Continued medication. Be sure to have an ample supply.

   (b) Regular visits to the clinic should be continued.

   (c) Refusal to take medicine, or side effects from medicine, should be reported to the doctor.

   (d.) High vitamin intake and high protein diet should be encouraged.

2. Socializing should be tactfully encouraged, but not insisted upon.

3. Work plans of an occupational therapy type should be planned: painting, cleaning, gardening, etc.

4. Daily exercise is helpful: walks, jogging, push-ups, knee bends, games.

5. Encourage attendance at selected motion pictures.

6. Suggest hot baths (soaks) prior to bedtime as a means of inducing sleep.

7. Plan meals that are high in protein, low in sugar, and free of caffeine.

8. In the family, discuss the illness in an open fashion at all times; after all a repaired brain is as good a topic of conversation as a recovery from double pneumonia.

9. The inner locks of the apartment or house should be made inoperative before the patient's return. This is particularly important if the patient was in the habit of retiring to the bedroom or bathroom and locking the door. Room doors, of course, may be closed, and all members of the family will respect privacy by learning to knock before entering.

10. A patient quickly learns that some degree of relief from the profound brain stimulation can be provided by the excessive use of nicotine, usually in the form of cigarette smoking. As he uses it, nicotine is not a stimulant but a tranquilizer. This habit must thus be tolerated while he is severely ill.

17. How Does the Patient Get Out of the Mental Hospital?

The exit varies with the type of hospital (whether private; veterans, or public) and the reversibility of the legal or signing process that got him into the hospital. If he is over age 21 and admitted to a private hospital on his own signature, then he is a voluntary patient and has the legal right to sign himself out. He is foolish to do so, however, unless his schizophrenia is under good control and unless he plans to continue the regime of therapy which has relieved his symptoms.

Getting out of a public hospital is usually much more difficult than the equally laborious process of getting into a public hospital—so the patient must have tolerance and patience. If he is over 21 years of age and has signed himself into the hospital, the exit process may be equally simple; that is, he may sign himself out. But he should not be foolish and leave before he is well enough to cope with the stresses of the outside world. He should plan to take advantage of the halfway house or clinic which may be affiliated with the hospital. He should also plan to join a local Schizophrenics Anonymous group or similar group, such as Recovery, Inc., if one exists in his locality. (See Chapter 19)

If he has been committed to a county or state hospital, then his stay in the hospital may be longer, but not necessarily more tedious. By actively engaging in the work and occupational therapy programs of the hospital, he will have ample opportunity to impress the hospital staff with his cooperation and stability. Needless to say, he should cooperate completely in the medical and group-therapy programs.

He may have been committed because society thought at the time that he would be safer and get well more quickly under enforced hospitalization. It is the purpose of hospital therapy to provide treatment until adequate social rehabilitation occurs. At this point a committee of the medical staff goes on record to the effect that the patient will be able to maintain his mental and physical health in the outside world. Usually a careful follow-up on his health is planned.

Discharges from public hospitals are made under the strictest controls. The physician in immediate charge makes the recommendation after careful evaluation of the patient's condition. The patient is then presented at a weekly staff conference. After this committee approves of the recommendation, the entire record comes before an administrator who makes the final decision. In some states, such as New York, a legal staff member must also approve.

It is not the purpose of a public institution to keep a patient beyond what is considered to be his maximum degree of social rehabilitation, but release does take time.

A useful mechanism for obtaining quicker release from a state or public hospital is the transfer to a private hospital. The private hospitals are more adequately staffed and, frequently, can more rapidly complete the numerous interviews, questionnaires for departure, and arrangements for continued therapy which are necessary for a patient's discharge. The political sensitivity and vulnerability of a public hospital may, frequently, make the decisions in the release of a patient most difficult.

18. Now That the Patient Is Out of the Hospital He must:

1. Realize that he is sick, cooperate with the doctor and follow his advice, and, above all, continue the medicines.

2. Realize this illness is no one's fault, including his own.

3. Not act or be influenced by his hallucinations.

4. Not discuss his hallucinations with anyone except his doctor.

5. Eat well and regularly.

6. Get plenty of rest and avoid fatigue.

7. Avoid stressful emotional reactions whenever possible.

8. Never use his illness as an excuse for ugly behavior.

9. If he has a relapse or a letdown, he should realize that this is a temporary condition. He recovered before, and he will recover again. The next relapse will be less severe.

10. When he is well, he should write down all his reasons for living, so when he feels badly, he can read his list again and be comforted.

19. Schizophrenics Anonymous (SA)

Whenever patients form a companionship group on the basis of their common disabilities, these groups are named for the disorder involved. SA is modeled after Alcoholics Anonymous (AA) a group which has proven its worth over a period of many years. SA maintains that it is not group therapy, since the group has no regular leader or therapist. Theoretically, at least, each member is of equal value. No one person can dominate the organization. A good description of Schizophrenics Anonymous is perhaps that of a fellowship of men and women who have all had a common experience— that of schizophrenia—and who get together as a group to *share* their common experience in order to help themselves and others get well. They differ from AA in that they tolerate and share experiences with various drug therapies which are needed for the social rehabilitation of the schizophrenic. The AA group, unfortunately, is usually against *any* drug therapy. We say unfortunate, since about 25 per cent of the alcoholics have schizophrenia as their basic problem and need antischizophrenic drug therapy.

20. *There Now Are Specific Antischizophrenic or Antipsychotic Drugs:*

"Almost all symptoms and manifestations characteristic of schizophrenic psychosis improved with drug therapy, suggesting that the phenothiazines should be regarded as 'antischizophrenic' in the broad sense. In fact, it is questionable whether the term 'tranquilizer' should be retained."

This is an exact quote from the report of the Collaborative Study Group, National Institute of Mental Health, U. S. Public Health Services, published in *Archives of General Psychiatry*, Vol. 10, p. 246, March, 1964.

Psychotropic drugs of this class have been called ataractic and neuroleptic. For some time they were described as the "major" tranquilizers to distinguish them from the "minors" of the antianxiety league. These agents are unrelated chemically to previously known sedatives. Pharmacologically, they differ in these respects: they do not produce anesthesia; they tend to *increase* muscle tone of the tongue and face and lower the convulsive threshold; and they have a negligible propensity for production of drug dependence or habit formation. As the group name implies, drugs of this kind have striking effectiveness in the treatment of psychoses, such as the schizophrenias. They are frequently useful in small doses as antianxiety agents, though their side effects limit their general usefulness.

In the early fifties, the first of these new drugs, chlorpromazine (Thorazine) and reserpine (Serpasil) were introduced. These are specifically *antipsychotic* in their effect. The best of the new drugs normalize the patient without producing sleepiness. They have revolutionized the treatment of schizophrenia and have slowly, but so positively, improved patients that most can now be treated in the medical sections of general hospitals. Let us summarize the effect in man of the three chemical classes of drugs now available.

The Oral Antischizophrenic Drugs

Chemical Class	Phenothiazine Type	Butyrophenone Type	Reserpine Type
(100)	Thorazine * (chlorpromazine)	(2) Haldol (haloperidol)	(2) Reserpine *
(100)	Mellaril *		
(50)	Compazine		
(10)	Trilafon		
(8)	Navane		
(5)	Stelazine		
(2)	Prolixin (fluphenazine)		
(2)	Permitil (fluphenazine)		
(X)	Equivalent antipsychotic dose. For example: 100 mgm. Thorazine = 2 mgm. Permitil		

* Most sedative or sleep-producing

The Intramuscular Antipsychotic Drugs

I.M. Prolixin enanthate‡ I.M. Haldol I.M. Reserpine

Thorazine or Trilafon are used routinely in the muscle to calm agitated patients. Intravenous Valium, Sparine or sodium Amytal may sometimes be used to calm agitation. These drugs are not perfect and any one or more of the following side effects may occur.

1. Tightening and contractions of the muscle of the tongue, face, or neck.*

2. Restlessness, such as floor pacing (apparent agitation).*

3. Tremor of the hands and arms.*

4. Blood disorders, such as decreased red or white count.

5. Yellow jaundice.

6. Psychiatric depression.

7. Convulsions.

These symptoms 4 through 7 are serious symptoms.

8. Increased sensitivity of the skin to sunlight.

9. Increase in appetite and body weight.

Some of these symptoms are simply annoying and will disappear with time. However, let the physician be the judge, since he has antidotes for many of the symptoms.

In addition to the above the antiepilepsy drugs, such as Dilantin, may be used in those patients who show abnormal brain waves or other neurological signs.

‡ (Long acting—single injection lasts 2 weeks)
* All of these muscle symptoms are relieved by Benadryl or Atropine.

Megavitamin Therapy:

Niacin (nicotinic acid) (B-3) was discovered as the antipellagra factor in 1935. Before 1950, Dr. Washbourne reported that students with emotional difficulties did better when given large doses of niacin. The first study on schizophrenics was done by Drs. Abram Hoffer and Humphry Osmond in 1952 to 1954. A controlled study was completed in 1954, which showed either niacin or niacinamide therapy to be better than dummy capsule therapy. In the next five-year period, the results showed:

	No.	No. Hospitalized	No. Suicide
Control patients	98	47	4
Niacin patients	73	7	0

The dose of vitamin needed is large, namely, 3.0 grams per day. Larger doses are, however, used to lower the blood cholesterol. The physician can also use niacinamide, since these large doses of niacin produce a reddening of the skin in the blush area. This flush is more severe in blonde patients and children, who may also complain of itching in the reddened area. In these patients, the doctors recommend niacinamide, which does not produce the reddening of the skin in the blush area. In older patients, however, niacinamide may produce sedation and psychiatric depression; and in all patients with large doses, some degree of irritation of the stomach may occur. In its extreme form this irritation produces nausea and vomiting.

Another report made by Dr. Vander Kamp, 1966 finds the schizophrenic needs much more vitamin C (ascorbic acid) then the normal. This is tested by the dose of vitamin C needed to spill out in the urine. Normals will do this promptly, but the schizophrenic will only spill "C" after large doses are given for several days. Since vitamin C can also be taken in large doses, the present supportive therapy used by physicians is the combined use of niacinamide and vitamin C. We do know that stress will remove vitamin C from the adrenal glands and we know that the patient after the stress of an operation may need more C. It may be thus supposed that the schizophrenic patient may require more because, with his brain stimulation, he is under constant stress. The need of the chronic schizophrenic for up to ten times more vitamin C has been confirmed by Dr. M. F. Ozerengin and his coworkers at Marcy Hospital, New York.

Dr. Linus Pauling, the double Nobel laureate, has recently joined those advocating megavitamin and megaprotein therapy for schizophrenia. "The proper functioning of the brain is known to require the presence in the brain of molecules of many different substances," he said. For example, mental disease usually associated with physical disease is known to occur when there are low concentrations in the body of any one of a number of vitamins, including the B-vitamins 1, 3, 6, and 12; biotin or vitamin H; ascorbic acid or vitamin C, and folic acid.

There are a number of arguments, he wrote, that support the idea that the optimum, or best amounts, of these normal but vital substances may be different from the amount provided by the diet or manufactured by the body, itself. In fact, the optimum amounts may be different from the minimum daily amounts necessary for life or recommended for good health.

The process of evolution doesn't necessarily guarantee that an organism will always produce the optimum amount of a vital substance. For instance, man and a few other primates, are among the rare mammals that don't manufacture ascorbic acid or vitamin C. Apparently, an ancestor common to man and other primates lost this ability about 20 million years ago when ascorbic acid became available in the diet, and a genetic mutation was able to survive and replace its ascorbic acid-making predecessor. The advantages of getting rid of the cell machinery needed to make ascorbic acid outweighed the disadvantages of receiving less than the optimum amount of the vitamin. Even if the amount of ascorbic acid in the diet declined in the past 20 million years to far less than the optimum amount, it's improbable the organism could regain its ability to make ascorbic acid, Dr. Pauling argued.

He explained that laboratory experiments with normal and mutant microbes not only support this thesis but indicate organisms do, in fact, survive and grow with less than the optimum amounts of vital nutrients or "nutrilites."

Role of Enzymes Noted:

It's also possible that a defective gene in an individual might result in less than the optimum amount of a vital substance, Professor Pauling reported. Most chemical reactions in the body are triggered by enzymes, chemical catalysts controlled by the cell's genes. The enzyme combines with some other substance, broadly called a substrate, and then the complex decomposes into the enzyme and new chemical products. The body produces enough substrate to saturate the enzyme and thus keep the chemical reactions going at just the proper rate.

However, a defective gene might lead to an enzyme that has a decreased ability to combine with a substrate. This would result in a less than normal rate of reactions. To get the reaction rate back to normal, one would need to supply more substrate, enough to, in effect, "soak up" the defective enzyme. According to Dr. Pauling, the substrate might be a vitamin, thus "a rationale for megavitamin therapy," he explained.

Deaner Therapy:

Deaner is an analogue of choline which passes from the blood to the brain better than choline. This is used by some physicians as supportive therapy in schizophrenia and autism. Choline is one of the water-soluble vitamins, so Deaner can be considered part of the megavitamin therapy. Some autistic children respond remarkably to Deaner, and the young child with a shortened attention span will also benefit.

Speed of Antipsychotic Drugs:

Heinz Lehmann, M. D., of Montreal, has summarized the anticipated speed of anitpsychotic drug action when used alone as follows:

1. Patient becomes cooperative within five days.

2. Socialization, but continued thought disorder, for up to two months.

3. Relief of thought disorder after six or more weeks.

4. Continued treatment for at least two years before stopping medication.

If used in a "total push" with megavitamin therapy, the patient can usually be discharged from the hospital in two to three weeks.

21. Other Standard and Proven Therapy for the Schizophrenias

Prior to 1935 patients were treated with sedative therapy, since this was the only treatment available. The sedation was produced by hot baths or packs, paraldehyde, sodium amytal, or morphine-scopolamine. These were given in rotation, since every means was needed to keep the patient from dying of acute psychotic exhaustion; and, in spite of sedative therapy, tube feeding, and hot packs, many did die.

In 1933, Dr. Manfred Sakel introduced insulin coma therapy, and in 1934, Dr. Ladislas J. Meduna introduced metrazol convulsive therapy. The latter was rapidly discarded when Dr. Cerletti and Dr. Bini (1938) found that a single convulsion could be safely produced by the application of an alternating current to the head. This is electroconvulsive therapy (shock, EST or ECT). With refinements, such as electronic control of the current, thiopental to produce amnesia, and other drugs to relax the muscles, EST has lost its side effects and is the treatment of choice for suicidal patients and the mainstay for weekly treatment of the severely schizophrenic patient, as well as for the schizophrenic patient who does not respond promptly to anti-psychotic drug medication.

These older therapies were erroneously criticised by some of the talking or listening therapists as being punishment rather than treatment, a misconception which has prevented many patients from receiving this effective treatment. These therapies are effective in preventing hospitalization, and, for those in hospitals, the stay is shortened. Moreover, this is the only form of treatment to which some suicidal patients respond rapidly, so that in these cases EST is truly life-saving.

After the year 1940, EST and insulin coma were the standard therapies for the schizophrenias. The general rule was to use insulin coma in the younger patients and EST in the older patients. Both of these therapies shortened hospitalization or produced complete remission of the disease in some patients. When given in moderation, such as no more often than every other day to the nondominant side of the brain (the right side in right-handed and the left side in left-handed patients), the treatment is well tolerated.

In Sweden, where the science and art of psychiatric practice and treatment is at a high level, the use of EST, plus drugs, to restore patients to a better degree of normality is still the routine. This is also the practice in many private mental and some public hospitals in Europe and the United States.

In regard to those therapies which started in 1936 and which are frequently called Somatic Therapies, the study of Dr. Odegard, based on statistics from the Norwegian hospitals, is pertinent. The discharge rate for mild schizophrenias was always good, but the stay was shortened by EST or insulin coma. The real change was in the severe schizophrenics who might otherwise have remained hospitalized for years or their lifetime. From 1915 to 1935, Norway had an intensive program of nursing care and occupational therapy for the schizophrenic, but the effect on the patients' discharge rate was not noticeable. He says: "This was the period of mental hygiene: prevention was stressed, because the prognosis was so bad for fully fledged mental disorders. The high hopes of a prevention have hardly been fulfilled even today, whereas the dramatic improvement in therapeutic results was quite unexpected. Starting from 1935, the discharge rate was doubled in five years, and in ten years it was trebled." This effect of EST and insulin coma has frequently been overlooked by some of the present generation of therapists.

Today one must adopt a philosophy of treatment wherein all therapeutic measures must be used in a progressive fashion to prevent hospitalization or restore the hospitalized patient to the community. One starts with talking therapy of a supportive nature, reduction of environmental stress, and megavitamin therapy. A second step is the use of antipsychotic drugs in addition to the vitamins, and, finally, the somatic therapies are used as a last resort, a retreat to prepared positions in the war against the schizophrenias.

22. Antianxiety Drugs in Schizophrenia

Drugs, such as alcohol, barbiturates, Miltown, Librium, Valium, Serax, Doriden, Noludar, chloral hydrate, paraldehyde, and many others, have a strong sedative or antianxiety effect. They may be useful in an emergency, and the physician may use them in conjunction with the more effective antipsychotic medication. Antianxiety drugs should not be used as the *only* medication for treatment of the schizophrenias. Fully one-fourth of the alcoholics are chronic schizophrenics, who have found that alcohol as a sedative in gross overdosage will give them a week-end of relief from their profound overstimulation.

As with alcohol, all antianxiety drugs have a varying degree of drug abuse (habit-forming) liability, which is not true of the antipsychotic drugs. Schizophrenics who are hooked on drugs, such as the short-acting barbiturates, have a double disorder, which may be difficult to diagnose and treat unless these patients are completely frank with their physician.

23. *Everyday Drugs and the Schizophrenic*

Most schizophrenics are overstimulated so that they have an increase in their symptoms when they knowingly or unknowingly take brain stimulants. Some of the common stimulants which may worsen the degree of schizophrenia are coffee or tea (because of caffeine), antihistamines (as in cold capsules), and amphetamines (Bennie pills or Methedrine, as in weight-reducing drugs). All stimulants should be avoided, and the patient should take Sanka rather than coffee, milk rather than tea, and orange juice rather than cola or similar beverages.

Some of the prescription drugs which may markedly increase brain stimulation are antidepressant drugs, the MAO inhibitors, and some local anesthetics, such as cocaine. These must be avoided except when the use is closely supervised by the physician.

Drugs such as buffered or simple aspirin are sedative to the brain, and these may be used freely for pains and mild sedation. The compounded aspirins, such as Anacin and APC tablets, contain caffeine and should be avoided.

24. Suggested Drug Therapy for the Schizophrenic Patient and Some Observations

1. As shown by their hyper-regulated brain waves and minimal response to sedative drugs, schizophrenic patients are obviously overstimulated. Therefore, we advise doctors not to use potent drug stimulants, such as amphetamines, Vivactyl, Tofranil, or Parnate. The stimulants which can be used with caution are Deaner, Triavil, Elavil, or Ritalin. Some patients respond to thyroid, and after two or three months of Lithium therapy, thyroid may be needed.

2. The dose of any drug is enough when it produces the desired therapeutic effect. Enough of a potent antipsychotic drug should be given to produce some side action, such as muscle symptoms, motor restlessness, or tremor. These side actions can be controlled by atropine-type compounds or Benadryl.

3. Benadryl or Mellaril should be prescribed as bedtime medication. These compounds have less suicide liability than barbiturates or barbiturate

substitutes, and they have enough atropine-like effect to reduce muscle symptoms of the Trilafon or Prolixin therapy.

4. Niacinamide, vitamin C, and Deaner should be used for children. It is very effective! As the child becomes more normally active and mischievous, Haldol concentrate (one to four drops each morning) may be needed and is highly effective.

5. The niacin, vitamin C treatment is recommended in treating an adult, because niacinamide may cause psychiatric depression. The skin flushing of niacin is reduced as therapy continues. Periactin is a dose of four mgs. given one hour before niacin will prevent the flushing and discomfort which occurs in the first four days of niacin therapy. The first dose of niacin should be between 50 and 100 mgs. Niacin may produce insomnia and may precipitate attacks of gout (acute rise in the serum uric acid) with nausea and vomiting. These attacks are self-limited because of the vomiting.

6. Drugs which may produce the side effect of psychiatric depression in the adult are niacinamide, Haldol and Stelazine.

7. One must pay heed to parents when they say they have another sibling who may need treatment. They are good judges, since they have lived with the disorder of schizophrenia.

8. Schizophrenia is frequently called "minimal brain damage" before puberty and "emotional disorder" after puberty. Objective psychometric tests, such as the HOD card-sort or the EWI, should be used to test for disperception in these patients. (HOD Test is the Hoffer-Osmond Diagnostic Test, and the EWI Test is the Experiential World In-

ventory, both explained earlier in this primer.)

9. Dilantin therapy is effective in some adult schizophrenia where intense mood changes and irritability are the presenting symptoms. In children with epileptic tendencies, and schizophrenia, Dilantin is most effective. Folic acid and niacinamide therapy may accentuate latent epilepsy.

10. Because of its rapid oral absorption, Mellaril (50 mg.) is preferable to Thorazine for calming the agitated patient. Mellaril is not ideal when used as the only antipsychotic medication, since the strong adrenergic blocking effect inhibits ejaculation in the male and may produce postural hypotension with fainting.

11. Patients not controlled by megavitamin and antipsychotic drugs can frequently be benefited by Lithium therapy.

12. An adequate treatment schedule for an adult might be:

Niacin	1 gram 3 x per day
Vitamin C	1 gram 3 x per day
Trilafon	8 mg. each a.m. and p.m. (or Haldol 1 mg. each a.m. and p.m.)
Mellaril	25 to 50 mg. at bedtime
Benadryl	50 mg. at bedtime
Vitamin E	200 units each a.m.
Pyridoxine	25 mg. each a.m.
Deaner	200 mg. each a.m.

Lithium should be added if full control is not obtained.

13. An adequate treatment schedule for a child might be:

Niacinamide	1 gram a.m. and p.m.
Vitamin C	1 gram a.m. and p.m.

Mellaril	25 mg. at bedtime (if needed)
Haldol concentrate	2 to 4 drops each a.m.—0.2 to 0.4 mg.
Pyridoxine	25 mg. each a.m.
Deaner	50 to 200 mg.each a.m.
Benadryl	50 mg. at bedtime (if needed)

25. A Summary of Treatment of Schizophrenia

The mild schizophrenic patient may respond well to small doses of nicotinic acid or nicotinamide with or without added vitamin C. For the almost normal individual the dose may be as low as 50 to 100 mg. each morning of niacin. This will produce skin flushing only when the individual is thoroughly relaxed as by a good night's sleep. The flush is not objectionable. Niacinamide on the other hand is more apt to produce feelings of sedation and depression, which may not be well tolerated by the almost well individual; and the depressed patient must certainly use niacin rather than niacinamide. If the patient has severe feelings of unreality (as verified by the HOD or EWI tests) larger doses of vitamins may be needed. These are excreted easily by the kidney if the body does not need them. Vitamins, however, are only supportive treatment, and the patient may complain that he feels the same in spite of the vitamins. These patients will need a major antipsychotic drug, such as Trilafon. Permitil, or Haldol. The last compound, Haldol, is more apt to produce feelings of depression than the first two. If the patient is agitated, then Thorazine or Mellaril is used for its antipsychotic and sedative effect. Of these two, Mellaril is better absorbed. The patient must frequently be given doses large enough to produce some muscle symptoms, such as tremor or muscle stiffness before maximum benefit results. These symptoms are antidoted by Benadryl in repeated dosage. One must, therefore, need to retreat to stronger therapy if the patient does not do well with mild therapy.

In spite of adequate drugs and vitamins, the patient may need more vigorous therapy, such as electroshock or insulin coma therapy; some patients require such somatic therapy once a week in order to stay out of the hospital. This should be arranged for in an outpatient clinic, since the hospitals presently available in the United States are not geared to give a patient weekly therapy in order to keep the patient at a maximal degree of remission. For the patient who will not take oral medication one must use Haldol concentrate orally (which has no taste and which can be put in any beverage). Occasionally these patients can be coaxed into accepting an intramuscular injection of Prolixin enanthate, which gives them adequate medication for a one- to two-week period.

We must remember that all psychiatric diagnoses are in a state of constant revision, with the doctors straddling the fence rather than committing themselves. They are waiting until some objective test will lead the way to a better and more standard diagnosis. Such objective tests will probably be based on some biochemical or immune chemical reaction and will provide insight into the cause and treatment of the schizophrenias. The most useful tests would be a simple saliva or urine test. If accurate, even a blood test or skin reaction test would be feasible for the mass screening of young adults.

26. What May Schizophrenics Do to Diminish Stress?

Move to a desert island, or become a hermit! These escapes have been used in the past, but the islands, caves, and isolated woodlands are becoming harder to find. Furthermore, self-isolation only reduces the stress from society and may increase physical and psychological stress. One patient became a successful merchant seaman, after finding that a ship was a warm place to live. The crew soon got accustomed to his peculiar habits and grimaces. He waited on tables, so he never had to work more than two hours at one time. This degree of stress he found was within his limit. He spent his spare time watching the ocean.

Some business and professional men learn to limit their work hours to the mornings, and some newspaper reporters learn that they can be their own boss and work within their limits of endurance by becoming effective and original freelance writers. The elimination of the travel to work and home each morning and evening will frequently help greatly to reduce the environmental stress.

Once the condition is understood by relatives they can help a great deal by not being overly argumentative or insisting that peculiar habits must be corrected or complexes talked out.

27. What About Those Psychedelic Drugs Like LSD and Marijuana?

The term psychedelic was coined by Dr. Humphry Osmond and means a mind-expanding drug. Pharmacologically these drugs are all profound stimulants which lead to hallucinations. Under the influence of these drugs, normal people may have hallucinations and revelations ("great truths"). After the drug wears off, the revelations may be recalled, but within a few days the great truths are neither great nor true. The drugs of this type have been used mainly in the experimental treatment of phobias, compulsions, and alcoholism. They are not useful in schizophrenia.

One group therapist states that he always likes to have at least one schizophrenic in each treatment group because "that patient cuts through the morass of stilted conversation and gets down to the basic issues." The schizophrenic is already over-stimulated and "turned-on" without any stimulant such as LSD. If given a stimulant, such as LSD or Methedrine (speed), the mild schizophrenic can have a real psychotic break that requires more than one day of hospitalization, whereas the effects of a standard dose of LSD on a normal person will always pass off in eight to twelve hours. An intravenous injection of Methedrine in the mild schizophrenic will also precipitate a psychosis which may last more than twenty-four hours. These turned-on patients usually wind up in the hospital emergency clinic for treatment. The use of these stimulants by the borderline schizophrenic indicates clearly that

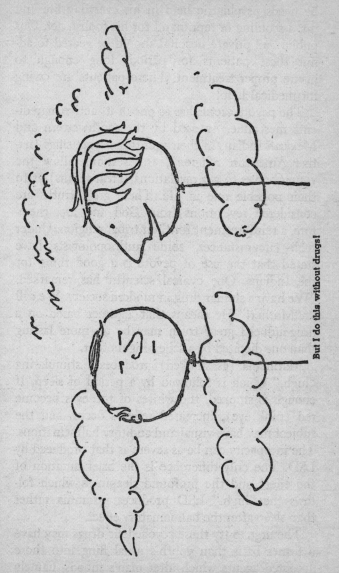

But I do this without drugs!

he needs psychiatric help in his everyday life and not a scolding or reprimand for his foolish act. Our public and private hospital should be geared to admit these patients for periods long enough to insure proper treatment. These patients are crying for medical help!

The peyote cactus has as one of its active ingredients mescaline. As used by the southwestern and Mexican Indians in their monthly peyote sings (native American religion), the sessions allow the young braves to get revelations (great truths) as to their possible role in life. These great truths are considered revelations from God and are, therefore, a reinforcement for their tribal religion. Under such circumstances, some anthropologists have stated that the use of peyote is a good thing for the Indians. One cynical scientist has remarked, "We have a similar drug in modern society. We call it "Mother!" He means that a career based on a drug-induced great truth may be no more lasting than one dictated by a scheming mother.

Marijuana (as smoked) produces a stimulating "high," which is followed by a period of sleep. If enough is smoked, the whites of the eyes become red (pink eye), increased reflexes occur, and the subject may have visual and auditory hallucinations. The incapacity can be as severe as that produced by LSD. The only difference is the brief duration of the effect and the profound sleepiness which follows the "high." LSD produces insomnia rather than sleep after the hallucinatory effect.

The urge to try these psychedelic drugs may have a firmer basis than youth's usual fling into those accepted agents which alter man's moods, namely

alcohol, tobacco, betel nut, and sex. The open re-
bellion may be a repudiation of talking therapy in
favor of the more potent drug therapy which has
evolved in the past ten years. The modern drugs
will lift depressions, control schizophrenia, produce
sleep, and elevate moods.

Modern youth is assailed with so-called healing
talk from crib to college. Some of this talk is necessary for training, particularly the occasional sharp
"No!" followed by a slap and, more often, the
approving "good boy or girl," followed by a hug.
However, the modern youth may receive talk instead of discipline and training and be referred an-
nually, for one reason or another, to the talking
specialists, until he is able to grow a beard. By this
time he is adequately toilet-trained, but not otherwise disciplined. He knows that, insofar as he is
concerned, talking therapy is water off a duck's
back, so he goes in for the more potent drug therapy
to change his unhappy and disillusioned mood and
to try to solve the problem of living with himself.

The hippies are not absolutely against talking
therapy; they do it constantly among themselves;
but they have learned all of the reasons, blessings
and maledictions—to such an extent that they may
be disillusioned with the talking therapy as elaborated by our best behavioral theorists, both modern
and ancient. With disillusion, only drugs are left,
and these are good because "they are *real*, man,"
as positive in their action as a karate chop to the
Adam's apple—and sometimes just as lethal.

That Methedrine ("speed") can produce hallucinatory states is well known from the post-World
War II experience in Japan, where the promiscuous

use of Methedrine under the name "wake-amine" resulted in numerous psychotic breaks which necessitated hospitalization. It is also known that mild schizophrenics can have a frank psychosis precipitated by intravenous amphetamines.

A naturally occurring "speed syndrome" in the schizophrenic can occur when he unwittingly or willfully discontinues his antipsychotic medication. That this practice is sufficiently common is apparent from the high rate of readmission of patients to our mental hospitals, "the revolving door policy" as termed by some critics.

The schizophrenic does not elaborate methedrine but does probably elaborate some other methylated amine, which acts as a natural brain stimulant. It follows that some patients will discover that they need less sleep and are temporarily more productive if they stop taking their antipsychotic medication. Of course, useful stimulation does not *always* result from stopping antipsychotic medication. Some patients may become rapidly psychotic.

In some, however, the stoppage of antipsychotic medication results in aggressive behavior. This is accompanied by a flight of ideas which is most highly prized by the intellectual, such as the artist, writer, or student who must live by his wits and original productivity. While he may appreciate the speed syndrome, he must also fully understand the consequences of overstimulation namely: paranoia or an even more serious degree of psychosis.

28. Sexual Interests and Activities of the Schizophrenic

Because of his inability to maintain a genuine interest in anyone the schizophrenic is usually extremely timid in sex. This is particularly true for the male who may remain content with masturbation as a form of sexual relief. Excessive and open masturbation can sometimes be controlled with Mellaril—a prescription drug. The male patient may give a history of no dating activity, bachelorhood, or late marriage. Since sexual union for the female is a more passive act her very timidity in this regard may result in more experience at sexual intercourse than that found in the male. The confused mind of the schizophrenic may also further a higher incidence of passive homosexuality in either sex. However, irrational fear of homosexuality is also common. The patient may sometimes try to manage this by falsely accusing others of sexual misdeeds.

A critical time for wise counseling in regard to sex occurs when a patient responds to drug therapy and desires some degree of normal love and sex interests. These patients have usually missed the tempering effect of high school dating, and their amateur approach to sex may result in further social rebuffs and emotional turmoil, even to the point of an unwanted pregnancy. If the female has accentuated feelings of unreality at or before the menstrual period, the use of birth control pills will smooth the ups and downs of her month-to-month living. The patient and physician should remember that occasionally birth control pills may have an undesirable effect on mood. The promiscuous schizophrenic female should be advised to have the insertion of an intrauterine contraceptive device.

29. Masturbation in the Schizophrenias

As previously stated, the rigid Victorian Age flavored the moral concepts to such an extent that juvenile masturbation was falsely alleged to cause schizophrenia. The boys were separated from the girls in high school for special lectures on sex in which the speaker vehemently and dramatically stated that the grey matter that surged from the stroked penis was the poor culprit's moral fiber and cerebral grey matter! Masturbation causes nothing but sleep, while such lectures lead to self-incrimination and neurosis!

Masturbation in both sexes is a method of relieving tension. This should be a normal part of the private life of young individuals. The most the parent might do, should he surprise the teen-ager in the act of masturbation, is to say, "That's a relief, isn't it!" Scolding may produce alienation and neurosis. As Dr. Sol Gordon has stated in his book (*Facts About Sex*, Charles Brown, Pub., 1969), "Masturbation is not physically harmful even when done often . . . if masturbation becomes compulsive, that is, not voluntary . . . then it is a sign of tension and upset. If it worries you, you may want to consult a psychologist or a psychiatrist."

The Princeton group has collected some male patients' reports on their speed of ejaculation. If the patient is low in blood histamine, then ejaculation will not occur with masturbation or at intercourse. If the patient is high in blood histamine the premature ejaculation may occur at sexual intercourse. Young teen-agers with a high blood histamine have reported that ejaculation may occur if they read a pornographic paragraph, or, in one case, if he hugs a girl! This hair-trigger action may result from excess histamine in the tissue mast cells in the head of the penis. These mast cells are present, and they store the histamine in all tissues of the body.

One can postulate that rubbing of the penis disrupts the mast cells so that the released histamine can then elicit a local reflex to cause ejaculation in the male. This is a fruitful area for research, much of which can be done in animals. When the male schizophrenic patient repeatedly fails to attain ejaculation, he may wrongly conclude that he lacks manhood, whereas, this is frequently the case in the low histamine schizophrenic, and the condition is corrected by adequate antipsychotic therapy. Sexual frigidity in the female may have a similar biochemical cause. Research in this field is needed to dispel the Freudian mythology that presently permeates the literature on frigidity in the female.

30. Sex Differences in Schizophrenia

The female is apparently more afflicted with schizophrenic-like disorders than the male; however, when the male is afflicted, his disorder may be harder to treat. This is based on the statistics prior to 1952 of schizophrenic patients in state hospitals where the figures show no great difference in the actual numbers of male and female schizophrenic

patients. However, marked differences existed in the
sex ratio of admissions with twice as many female
as male admissions. Two reasons may be given for
these two discordant statements. The female responds better to treatment, and she can be returned
to a family with greater ease and less social responsibility. Thus, prior to 1952, the majority of the
male patients who were hospitalized stayed in the
hospital longer than the female group of patients.
In contrast, the male patient may not get to the
hospital, but may actually go to jail instead. Any
parent who has tried to discipline, treat, or even
talk to a hostile and paranoid son will understand
that some male schizophrenic patients will frequently run afoul of the law and end up in jail
rather than in a hospital.

Our better jails recognize this and, frequently, do
an excellent job of treating the incarcerated male
schizophrenic patient.

One should note that juvenile autism (fantasy or
introverted thought), which may be a subtype of
schizophrenia, is four times more prevalent in boys
than in girls. This again is characterized by overstimulation of the brain and is presently difficult
to treat, although some do respond to niacinamide
and vitamin C and some to Deaner (see Childhood
Schizophrenia and Autism. Chapter 49)

31. The Four Seasons and the Schizophrenias

Schizophrenics may be born in any of the four
seasons. Recently Drs. Hare and Price reviewed the
birth month of all patients admitted to Bethlem-

Maudsley Hospital in London for the period 1951-63. They found that neurotic patients, as with a normal population, have significantly more birth months in the spring, while the schizophrenics were more apt to be born in the winter quarter. The reason is not known, but they speculate as follows: (1) greater robustness in the winter-born schizophrenic child, (2) protein deficiency in the mother's summer diet, or (3) vitamin C deficiency in the child born in the winter.

Yet another factor might be the lessening of the schizophrenic process in the mother or father during the warmer months of the year. January, February, and March are usually the worst months for the adult schizophrenic. Sexual activity might, therefore, be expected to be greater in April, May, and on into summer, as the schizophrenic process lessens and the patient feels better.

32. Schizophrenics, Alcohol and Barbiturates

The schizophrenic may attempt to drown his overstimulated brain with alcohol. It is estimated that 30 per cent of drug addicts and 25 per cent of male chronic alcoholics actually have schizophrenia as their basic trouble. They frequently are periodic alcoholics who get intoxicated for the weekend as the stimulation of a job becomes unbearable by Friday night. We find that many male chronic schizophrenics when finally hospitalized volunteer the information that they did try large doses of alcohol, but found that this made them sick. Some also find that the rebound from acute alcoholism adds fuel to the fire of overstimulation. This will happen when any short acting depressant, such as alcohol, barbiturates, or other sleeping pills, is used to treat schizophrenics.

These are habit forming, so that the patient cannot abruptly stop taking them without becoming seriously ill.

A further drawback is that either alcohol or barbiturates may destroy reserve and defenses so that the schizophrenic becomes frankly paranoid—suspicious of everything. This phenomenon is graphically portrayed in the belligerent drunk, who shows paranoia with his strong desire to fight.

Finally, barbiturates are dangerous because they often are used for suicide, or are the causes of accidental death through overdosage. Their effects are additive with those of alcohol, and the combination has killed many. In contrast, the antipsychotic drugs are not habit forming, nor are they nearly as lethal as the barbiturates when taken in a single large dose.

33. Endocrine Factors in the Schizophrenias

We know a great deal about the biochemistry of stress, but thus far none of the knowledge can be linked definitely to the biological cause of any of the schizophrenias. Because of profound overstimulation, the schizophrenic is constantly in a state of internal stress. Furthermore, because of mental turmoil and inability to relate to others he may be subjected to external stress as well as internal stress.

Stress is known to produce the following:

1. Depletion of vitamin C from the adrenals.

2. Increased urinary excretion of calcium, potassium, phosphate, uric acid, and steroid and adrenalin fragments.

3. Muscular fatigue, weakness, and dizziness.

4. Low sugar tolerance.

All of the above occur in schizophrenia and may need to be treated symptom by symptom. However, the stress is not the cause of schizophrenia, but rather the result of the overstimulated brain. In addition to treatment of the stress many individuals learn to reduce their environmental stress by living restricted lives.

In regard to stress and the senses, the occurrence of deafness in the adult may lead to personality changes of a paranoid nature. Blindness, a far greater affliction (either in the adult or child), does not result in schizophrenia. This alone would argue against environmental change as the cause of the disease.

Most of the known endocrine glands (even the large bowel) have been surgically removed from schizophrenics without improvement. We can recall cases of:

1. Self castration without benefit.
2. Removal of adrenal glands without benefit.
3. Thyroidectomy without benefit (except where mania is caused by the hyperthyroidism). But hypothyroidism also can cause psychosis which responds promptly and completely to thyroid extract.

Some have noted the facial hair growth on hospitalized female schizophrenics and postulated anterior pituitary or adrenal dysfunction. It is true that a small proportion of the female patients do have a tendency to excessive hair growth, but so do many of the fairer sex who are not mentally ill; they keep this tendency under control by cosmetic measures, as do the patients when they recover.

Many glands of the body have not been adequately studied in regard to schizophrenia. These are the pituitary, pineal, pancreas, prostate, and thymus. The possible significance of all the glands in postpartum psychosis (psychosis after childbirth) has not been determined.

34. Biochemical Theories

In the past the schizophrenias were sometimes blamed for juvenile masturbation. Also, toxins from the large bowel or inadequate detoxification by the liver were postulated. As psychoanalysis gained ascendency in the forties, the useful biological studies of the thirties died on the vine, not only because of the lack of money for further research, but also because the psychiatrists in charge of schizophrenics feared that taking any biological measurement, such as blood or spinal fluid, might disrupt talking therapy and make the insane more hopelessly insane. This still may hold true in many hospitals where the administrator, who has the final say, holds his post because of training in the theories of Freud or psychoanalysis.

With the advent of the effective antipsychotic drugs, reserpine and Thorazine, new theories for the biological defects in the schizophrenias have evolved. Reserpine removes serotonin (a primary

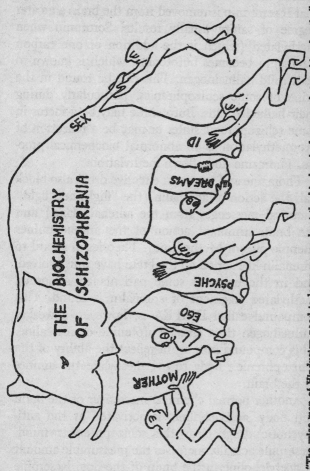

"The wise men of Hindustan need to learn more about the biochemical approach to schizophrenia."

amine) from the brain and LSD-25, the action of serotonin on smooth muscle. These original observations have not resulted in a quick answer, except that if serotonin is removed from the brain a greater degree of sanity usually results. Serotonin when methylated (which is the addition of one carbon fragment) becomes bufotenine, which is known to be a mild hallucinogen. This can be found in the urine of some schizophrenics, particularly during their hallucinations. Bufotenine may be a factor in some schizophrenic states or may be a reflection of overmethylation as an abnormal biochemical process. Thorazine slows down methylation.

Thorazine and the other effective drugs also block half the action of adrenalin (the "flight and fight" chemical messenger from the adrenal gland) and the brain stimulant action of the amphetamines (Bennie pills or Methedrine). Theories in regard to adrenalin-like action on the brain have thus evolved, and in the urine of some patients an abnormal methylated fragment of adrenalin is found. This compound called DMPEA is, however, a weaker hallucinogen than either bufotenine or mescaline. This compound may again reflect the ability of the schizophrenic's body to overmethylate the amines of the brain.

Another normal chemical messenger of the brain and body, acetylcholine, is activated as the antipsychotic drugs clear the schizophrenic's mind. Reserpine actually increases the measurable amount of acetylcholine in the brain of the dog. Reserpine also produces symptoms of acetylcholine overactivity in patients. The symptoms are lowered blood pressure and pulse and an increase in saliva. Most effective drugs may also produce a tremor of the hands and an increase in muscle tone. These are symptoms of acetylcholine excess. The use of Deaner as supportive therapy in the schizophrenic is based on the possibility that a more normal manufacture of acetylcholine may occur. Of the possible chemical messengers in the brain both acetylcholine and histamine deserve much greater study. Owing to the original biochemical finding on reserpine, too much of the laboratory study to date has been concentrated on serotonin and adrenalin. Overmethylation of the amines of the brain is the most logical biochemical defect which might explain the symptoms of the schizophrenic. This may not be due to the presently well studied amines (adrenalin or serotonin) but may be due to the little studied amines histamine, spermidine or spermine, or other amines.

The polyamines, spermidine and spermine, are of interest because we know:

1. They are elaborated by active glandular function, such as the prostate gland at puberty and the milk-producing breast after the birth of a baby.

2. These polyamines, particularly spermine, act as patterns or molds for the building of ribonucleic acids (RNA)—a substance which is probably synthesized constantly to provide the brain with a memory mechanism.

The flooding of the body with more polyamines in the pubertal and postpartum periods coincides with the natural history of periods of increased schizophrenic behavior. Dr. Venelin Iliev of Princeton has shown that spermine increases in the female with puberty. The methylated and substituted spermine and spermidines deserve study as possible stimulant and hallucinogens. Preliminary studies by the Princeton group indicate that a high level of spermidine correlates positively with abnormal ideation and disperception of time in the schizophrenic.

35. Abnormal Histamine Levels in Some Schizophrenics

Histamine has been suspect since the majority of schizophrenics do not have allergies, such as hay fever, asthma, or hives. According to Dr. Leblanc, of Montreal, tissue mast cells which contain histamine are few and attain a high level as the schizophrenic symptoms are relieved by antipsychotic drugs. Perhaps during the psychosis some of the histamine is being methylated to produce a more stimulating compound affecting the brain. Dimethyl histamine is more stimulating than histamine when tested in rabbits. It has not been tested in man for its possible hallucinogenic effect.

Recently Drs. Kremzner and Carl Pfeiffer of Princeton clarified the method for the determination of tissue histamine levels. When this method is used on the blood of schizophrenics (95 per cent of the histamine is in the dark staining basophil cells) then one-half of the untreated schizophrenic patients show decreased blood histamine. Drs. Iliev and Pfeiffer say this may account for their lack of allergic symptoms and may correlate with the mental state. They term these low histamine patients *histapenic* and distinguish them from suicidal adult schizophrenics who show a high blood histamine. These latter patients are called *histadelic,* because they have too much histamine in their blood and, presumably, in their brains.

A composite case history of a histapenic patient can be constructed as follows: a hyperactive child who is unnaturally healthy. For example, the rest of the family may get head colds, but the histapenic patient either misses the cold, or the virus infection fails to produce a rhinitis. (This natural resistance to virus infections may be the genetic advantage factor which has kept schizophrenia from disappearing over the ages). He is hypoallergic and sneezes only reflexly as when he moves to bright sunlight. He may have serious bruises, but does not complain of pain. A venous blood sample may be obtained with little or no sign of pain. He is hard to train, because a slap causes little pain. The patient is constantly active and sleeps poorly. With the hyperactivity, the patient may show compulsive stereotyped movements. Ideation, thought processes, and speech may be delayed in development or bizarre. His attention span is short, and learning is poor. Although his ability in some spheres may be high when tested, a high degree of disperception will be present in many spheres, such as sensory, time, body, self, and perception of others. Older patients will be depressed and/or confused by their disperceptions. These older patients may show paranoia and hallucinations. The quantitative EEG will show a high degree of brain wave over-regulation, so that the standard deviation of the EEG will be very low—perhaps less than half that of the normal.

Finally, the blood histamine will be below the normal level of 40 ng/ml.

The histadelic patient presents herself as one who is unhappy and has a blank mind. An intense preoccupation with suicide occurs frequently. The patient is referred to as being schizophrenic, although the first interview may give the initial impression that the patient has a neurotic or psychotic depression. However, the EWI and MMPI tests disclose schizophrenia with psychotic depression and suicidal tendencies. The past history shows that ECT and/or insulin therapy has not provided lasting benefit. The usual procedures, such as antipsychotic medication, will improve the patient to a definite plateau, but no further. This may be inadequate since unreality, blank mind, and depression persist, although the patient does not have hallucinations or paranoia. Usually the majority of these patients are female, although this adult preponderance may merely indicate the greater efficiency of the male patient in his suicide procedures. A mild degree of histadelia probably characterizes the addiction personality, but this suggestion must await chemical characterization of the blood of the addict. When all else (ECT, insulin and antipsychotic drugs) fails, the patient may respond slowly to small doses of Methadone given at bedtime. When we consider the alternatives, then Methadone becomes a lifesaving drug. Before starting therapy, Methadone treatment should be discussed fully with the patient and responsible relatives. The main side effect of Methadone therapy is nausea when these patients are also receiving antischizophrenic drugs.

The histadelic patient shows a blood histamine

level greater than 60 ng/ml. (Normal blood histamine level is 40 to 60 ng/ml). Approximately 20
per cent of the so-called schizophrenics fall into this
class. The differences and similarity of the histapenic and histadelic patients have been tabulated
in Table I. This is a new finding, and many of
these observations await confirmation. One should
note that these observations leave unexplained a
full 30 per cent of those patients with a normal
histamine level. However, the schizophrenias need
subdividing, and the high and low histamine concept has already resulted in more logical treatment
for each of these types.

**Table I—Differences in the Clinical Symptoms and
Responses of Low and High Blood Histamine Patient**

	Histapenia	Histadelia
Psychiatric Symptoms	(50%)	(20%)
Depression	1 +	4 +
"Blank Mind"	1 +	4 +
Thought Disorder	4 +	2 +
Paranoia	3 +	1 +
Hallucinations	4 +	1 +
Metabolic Differences		
Headaches	1 +	4 +
Fat Distribution	Stalagmitic	Normal
Speed of Ejaculation		
(sexual intercourse)	Slow	Fast
Reaction to pain	1 +	4 +
Dental Caries	4 +	1 +
Salivary Flow	1 +	4 +
Head colds (symptoms)	None	Normal
Skin Pigmentation	Fair	Normal
Allergies	Rare	Common
EEG Overarousal	4 +	4 +

| Familial Disorder | 1 + | 3 + |
| Age at Onset | Any | Adult |

Responses to Therapy

Antipsychotic Drug R_x	3 +	1 +
Niacin/Vitamin C	3 +	1 +
Folic Acid 2.5 mgm./day	Sometimes good	Worsens
High Protein Diet	Yes	No
ECT/Insulin	3 +	1 +
Methadone	0	3 +

36. The Sex Hormones and the Schizophrenias

Testosterone therapy is being used by Dr. Carl Pfeiffer in high blood histamine (histadelic) female schizophrenic patients. After much research this seems to have a sound scientific basis. Dr. M. L. Schearer and his team, in an article in *The Journal of Psychiatric Research* (Volume 5, page 349, 1967), showed that females who developed psychosis in the first month of pregnancy invariably had girl babies. Severely ill schizophrenic females, who carried male babies, had the pregnancy end in miscarriage or a still birth. Dr. M. A. Taylor and Dr. Robert Levine working at Manhattan State Hospital confirmed this in an article in *Science* (Volume 164, May 9, 1969) and also stated that the bearing of a female child worsens schizophrenia, while a male fetus improves the mother's psychotic state during the gestation period. If the baby is carried to full term the birth is usually followed by a postpartum psychosis which, however, will respond to testosterone therapy.

When this knowledge is coupled with the fact that autism is probably a schizophrenic process and that four out of five autistic children are males, we have a rather grim picture of the male fetus or child in relation to the schizophrenic mother. There are four obvious possibilities: (1) early miscarriage, (2) still birth at full term, (3) congenital defects, (4) juvenile autism, and (5) schizophrenia in the young adult years. One should remember that in any population the birth-rate shows that females are more numerous, usually 52 per cent female compared to 48 per cent male.

At Manteno State Hospital in Illinois there was a female schizophrenic who had had postpartum psychoses after the birth of her two male children. The first psychosis responded to electroshock therapy, while the second illness did not. After 15 years of hospitalization she recovered from her psychosis at the menopause—an event which is known to be marked by decreased estrogen and a relative increase in testosterone. This patient was one who would have responded to testosterone therapy or an artificial menopause. How many other women are now hospitalized with postpartum psychosis and have to await the menopause to relieve their abnormal ideas and disperception?

At the 1969 meeting of the Society for Biological Psychiatry, Dr. Lauretta Bender, a scientist who has devoted her lifetime to the study of autistic children, reported on the adulthood follow-up of 100 autistic children who now range in age from 22 to 45 years. As is usual with autistic children, the sample contained a naturally high preponderance of males—in this instance 80 males and 20 females.

Sixty-three per cent of these patients were institu-
tionalized while thirty-seven percent were in the
community. Some remissions occurred at puberty
for boys (testosterone therapy!), but none occurred
in the females. (Perhaps testosterone should be
tried.) These 100 patients had 215 mentally ill
relatives. In their adult schizophrenic disorder they
showed all of the classical types of schizophrenia,
including catatonia and paranoia. On the brighter
side of the picture 5 out of 100 of these unique
patients had earned graduate degrees at college, and
two had earned a Ph.D. degree. Dr. Bender stated
that special schools are important, as is a close
symbiotic relationship of the child to an understanding adult. When EST is used it is most effective at puberty when one might combine it with
testosterone therapy.

37. Schizophrenia as an Auto-Immune Response

Dr. Robert Heath of Tulane University has pioneered in the study of abnormal proteins in
schizophrenia and has recently reported that abnormalities can be produced in rabbits by making
the rabbit sensitive to extracts of its own brain. He
proposes that this may be a mechanism for the
production of one of the schizophrenic states. This
would explain the manufacture by the body of
an hallucinogenic protein, which he has described
and named Taraxein and which he believes is an
antibody to the septal region of the brain. He has
also shown that a small dose of histamine will produce symptoms of schizophrenia in the monkey

when this is injected into the septal area. This area is just back of the frontal lobes of the brain and is an area which relays man's moods to the rest of the brain. It is known that tumors of the frontal lobes sometimes produce a continuous happy mood similar to that of lobotomy—an operation which is no longer used for schizophrenia, but may still be used for the intractable pain of cancer. Dr. Heath has also found epileptic-like spikes in the depth-brain waves from the septal area of the schizophrenic. One must, therefore, agree that an auto-immune effect may be responsible for *some* schizophrenic states. This theory cannot be accepted as a cause of *all* schizophrenic states for the following reasons: (1) The effective antischizophrenic therapies, such as drug, ECT, and insulin coma are not known to suppress any immune responses, (2) The schizophrenic is hypoallergic. For example, he has less hay fever—only three per cent vs. 13 per cent for employees in the same community, (3) Schizophrenia has a completely different natural disease history from that of other suspected brain auto-immune diseases, such as rabies vaccine reaction and multiple sclerosis. Two other groups, one headed by Dr. John Bender of the Worchester Foundation and the other, Dr. Jaques Gottlieb, of Detroit, have exchanged samples of schizophrenic serum and have found that a high percentage of patients have an abnormally high level of alpha-2-globulin.

This globulin could be high because of some abnormal auto-immune response.

38. The Hypoglycemic Syndrome

Under endocrine factors we mentioned the pancreas and glucose-tolerance curves in the schizophrenic. Some patients have a syndrome of low blood pressure, headache, dizziness, sweating, nausea, and feelings of unreality—usually three to four hours after eating. This is relieved by food and, frequently, prevented by use of a high protein diet (meats, fish, cheese, and eggs).

The study of glucose tolerance in the schizophrenic has an interesting history. In the 1940's, it was known that double the usual sugar intake in a test would result in either a flat curve or a 20 per cent fall below the control level in the fifth to sixth hour of the test. Those schizophrenics with the flat curve are also resistant to insulin and have been labeled oneirophrenics by Dr. Ladislas J. Meduna. When ill they have a dreamlike state and respond better to therapy than others. However, too much has been made of this hypoglycemic syndrome by some physicians, who overtreat it with adrenal cortical extracts. Actually the disorder responds very well to a high protein and low sugar diet.

39. Is It Schizophrenia or Psychomotor Epilepsy?

One of the alternate diagnoses for patients with episodic schizophrenic behavior is psychomotor epilepsy. This is usually accompanied by a brain wave which shows trains of six per second positive spikes in the area of the temporal lobe. If no brain wave abnormality occurs, however, then the diagnosis must rest on the periodicity of the attacks, and drug tests which may give some clues. Seizures which are most likely to be mistaken for psychiatric disorders are attacks of local brain origin in which sensory experiences or psychical alterations constitute a prominent part of each attack or, occasionally, the entire attack.

Among the difficult diagnostic problems are sensory seizures of the areas of the brain that tell where the muscles and limbs are located. For example, the patient may describe attacks in which a limb feels enlarged, moves involuntarily to an awkward posture, or feels detached from the rest of the body. Focal sensory seizures may consist of visual or auditory experiences. Visual illusions (for example, objects in the environment appear too bright, too large or small, or out of shape) or similar distortions of auditory stimuli may be experienced. Highly organized hallucinatory attacks may occur in which the victim revisualizes a scene or a human form or hears music.

Psychical seizures consisting of transient, recurrent episodes of an abnormal idea may occur in isolation or in association with muscle or sensory epileptic phenomena. The feeling of strangeness or unreality or undue familiarity toward the surroundings during an attack is well known. Other delusions referable to time or environment (time rushes by or stands still) and delusions of derealization—depersonalization, in which one feels detached from his environment or from his own body—may represent epileptic phenomena. Epileptic seizures not infrequently may have emotional content. Frequently, the diagnosis is difficult, and the patient may be classified as schizophrenic. A valuable tool in the diagnosis is the therapeutic use of antiepileptic drugs, such as Dilantin, which may markedly benefit the psychomotor seizures, whereas Dilantin has little or no effect in schizophrenia. Thus. if Dilantin relieves the attack then the phenomenon is probably epileptic in origin.

40. Evidence For the Theory of Overstimulation in Schizophrenia

Dr. L. Goldstein of Princeton has shown by statistical analysis that the brain waves of the chronic male schizophrenics are relatively nonvariant, or hyperregulated. This and other abnormalities are characteristic of a continued over-alertness or state of overstimulation and distinguish the schizophrenic from the normal subject, who has hyperregulated brain waves only under the influence of LSD-25 or other profound stimulants. Dr. A. A. Sugerman and his colleagues have shown that treatment of schizophrenic patients with Thorazine or Trilafon is accompanied by a return of the brain waves to the normal range of variation and that the degree of schizophrenic behavior and overstimulation is decreased.

Dr. Goldstein has also shown that doses of one ug/kg of LSD-25, given to normal volunteers, causes hyperregulation of the brain waves, which then resemble the brain waves of the schizophrenic. This is because LSD-25 is a profound, and probably specific, brain stimulant. All the hallucinogens have been shown to be brain stimulants in rabbits.

The use of antidepressants has given rise to a new side action as a result of the brain stimulation which accompanies overdosage. Thus a schizophrenic psychosis may develop upon treatment of a depressed patient who previously had frequent episodes of depression, but no episodes of schizophrenia. Similarly, a recent study of such stimulants in schizophreics under blind test conditions has shown that these medications will make schizophrenics significantly worse. A study of an antidepressant by the Princeton group showed that as the quantitative brain waves became more hyperregulated, the behavior of the schizophrenic patients worsened. The use of iproniazid as a stimulant was in part the direct outgrowth of the euphoria and stimulation seen in tuberculous patients treated with this, which in overdosage produced a psychotic state.

Dr. Pfeiffer, of Princeton, has shown by both behavioral and objective EEG (electroencephalogram) data that schizophrenics can tolerate a cerebral depressant, such as an oral dose of 200 mg. of pentobarbital, better than can the normal volunteer. In contrast, as judged by emotional outbursts, the schizophrenic tolerated one ug/kg of LSD-25 less well than the normal volunteer.

In February, 1968, at a meeting in New York, three different groups of investigators essentially agreed with Dr. Goldstein that the schizophrenic is overstimulated both from behavioral and brain wave evidence.

1. Dr. Venables, of England, has presented evi-

dence for overstimulation, which has been confirmed by Dr. Kornetsky, of Boston.

2. Dr. Marjerrison, of Canada, also finds the brain waves of the schizophrenic to be hyperregulated, and furthermore, the degree of arousal anxiety increases when the patients have periods of hallucinations.

3. Dr. Enoch Calloway, of San Francisco, states the quantitative brain wave is a useful index of arousal anxiety which is present in the schizophrenic (even when sitting with eyes open), and he agrees that the so called withdrawn unresponsive chronic schizophrenic is extremely aroused. He is unresponsive only because he is pushed to the limit.

The schizophrenic patient has long been known to be an insomniac. This insomnia may precede the psychosis, extend through catatonic states, and be evident in the hospital wards at night if the patients are not treated with tranquilizers. Preliminary brilliance or prepsychotic stimulation may be one of the first signs of a psychotic break. The psychosis of prolonged wakefulness may also provide a similar example of the psychogenic effect of forced overstimulation which is physically induced. While no quantitative data are available, the brain waves of prolonged wakefulness are, by inspection, similar to that of the schizophrenic. Thus, these various observations would indicate that the schizophrenic is, indeed, in a chronic overstimulated state.

This overstimulation does not respond to the usual doses of barbiturates, alcohol, or other anti-anxiety drugs. The patient can be sedated by means of adequate dosage of the truly antischizophrenic drugs, such as Thorazine, reserpine or Haldol. These drugs oversedate the normal individual.

41. Malvaria and the Urinary Mauve Factor

Some schizophrenic patients excrete a biochemical in the urine which when separated on blotting paper can be made to turn lavender or mauve in color. This is the mauve factor of Hoffer, who claims it to be present in a high percentage of untreated cases. Dr. Abram Hoffer has used the term malvaria for this group of patients. He finds these patients respond more quickly and completely to megavitamin therapy with niacin and vitamin C. With the megavitamin therapy, the mauve spot disappears. The studies are still at the research level, and a mauve test is not needed in order to treat successfully most schizophrenics. The test may be of value as a research tool to distinguish clearly childhood schizophrenia. The chemical nature of the mauve factor, when established, will give an important clue to a possible biochemical abnormality in one type of schizophrenia.

42. Do Some Schizophrenics Have a Characteristic Odor?

Many of the older psychiatrists who treated schizophrenics noted that a distinctive odor accompanied the acute disease and that this odor disappeared with effective treatment. Most of the research work has been confined to the study of sweat, although the characteristic odor may also be present on the breath. Doctors and mothers are accustomed to noting acetone on the breath of a child with fever or diabetes, and, therefore, the *fruity odor* of the breath of some younger schizophrenics should not go unnoticed. The odor is sweet and similar to that of an aldehyde such as acetaldehyde or a chemical ester.

Dr. Kathleen Smith of St. Louis has made a study of the sweat from the clean skin of schizophrenics. The odor could not be detected by chemical methods, but rats could be trained to perform for a food reward on presentation of sweat from schizophrenics. This odor is attributed to normal skin bacteria by another group of investigators. Quite obviously additional studies are needed on the odor of the sweat of schizophrenics, and more thought should be given to the use of breath analysis as a possible test for the types of schizophrenia.

43. Body Build and the Schizophrenias

The lean gangling male or asthenic individual has frequently, in the past, been pinpointed as the body type preferred as a nest for the schizophrenic process. In contrast, the fat man was supposed to be lazy, jolly, and sleepy. We now know these generalizations to be in error. This error is apparent in that at least two types of drugs; namely, Thorazine and reserpine, will sometimes increase the weight of thin, chronic male schizophrenics without improving their schizophrenia. These are the rare occasions when the antipsychotic drugs work mainly on the body and to a lesser degree on the mind. The drug-induced increase in weight may be so great as to necessitate a reducing diet to control the weight gain.

Compared to the underweight individual, the overweight individual has the advantage of a large mass of fat, which can act as a sponge or "buffer tissue" to absorb and slowly release the fat-soluble drugs and biochemicals which act on the brain. Two examples are the anesthetics, such as ether, alcohol, or pentothal and the stimulants, such as the amphetamines. Obviously, the fat man can drink much more alcohol than the thin man and not get as drunk, and the anesthetist learns to use more anesthetic to allow for saturation of the fat of the patient. The fat man or woman can also take more stimulant whether coffee, "speed," or "Bennie pills" and not get as stimulated, maniacal, or "turned on."

Since we postulate an inner stimulant from the cells of the body which overstimulates the brain to cause schizophrenia, the brain stimulant effect is based on the fat soluble nature of this stimulant and is undoubtedly modified by the amount of body fat available. Thus, the fat paranoid patient is apt to be a productive insomniac, who can be exceedingly active and may be more hypomanic than paranoid. The same degree of abnormal stimulation, if occurring in the thin individual, results in severe insomnia and, perhaps, hospitalization for paranoia or other schizophrenic symptoms.

Some people, not ordinarily classifiable as schizophrenic, have learned for themselves, by crash diets, that the thin state is not the best for them. Obviously their fatty tissue acts as a buffer to pick up abnormal stimulants and gives them a more productive and livable personality. The productivity and originality of some of our uncouth, large, over-weight, eccentric characters is thus positively amazing to their friends, but the secret may really be that a mild schizophrenic process plus body fat makes them productive and original.

44. Self Evaluation: The Psychoanalysts Look into Their Complacent Mirrors

The American Psychoanalytic Association, in the October, 1967, issue of its *Journal* has released findings of a long-term sociological and statistical study of psychoanalytic practices and the comparative results of treatment by psychoanalysis and psychotherapy, respectively. This is summarized in the *A.P.A. News.*

As judged by Dr. Weinstock and Dr. Hamburg, who headed the evaluation committees, the group of 10,000 patients treated by psychoanalysis were 96.6 per cent satisfied with their improvement obtained over one- to four-year periods. The analysts judged that 97.3 per cent of the patients were "improved in total functioning." While this sounds good, one should note that the relief of symptoms *in chronic male schizophrenics* was only 9 *per cent,* and the over-all rate of symptom cure was only 27 per cent. In contrast, the spontaneous remission rate from the first attack of schizophrenia was 25 to 30 per cent in males, and the hospital discharge rate for male schizophrenics treated by all available methods was a whopping 76 per cent. The 9 per cent, therefore, confirms the impracticality of treating schizophrenia by psychoanalysis. No mention was made of patients who got worse under analysis and had to be hospitalized. Neither was any mention made of the suicide rate—an unavoidable contingency which always plagues psychiatric practice.

The investigators were forthright in pointing out the limitations of the findings and the methodology employed. Nevertheless, some new sociological information is available. For example:

Fifty-seven per cent of the patients studied had incomes under $10,000; 25 per cent, from $10,000 to $20,000; and 15 per cent, more than $20,000. (The minimal cost of a year of analysis is approximately $5,000).

Nearly all (98.8 per cent) were white and included Protestants and Jews in about equal numbers; only 10 per cent were Catholic or of other denominations.

Twenty-two per cent had been to high school, 41.9 per cent to college, and 35.8 per cent to graduate school. Since this adds to 100 per cent, one can infer that at least a high school education is needed for a patient to understand the workings of the mind as disclosed by psychoanalysis.

Forty-four per cent were in analysis for less than a year, 33 per cent for two years, and 11.3 per cent for four years or more.

They state that psychoanalysis was found to be significantly more effective in adjudged improved character structure than was psychotherapy. However, no similar group of patients receiving drug therapy or only psychotherapy was included, nor was the evaluation done by "controlled tests."

The authors of the report venture that this first evaluation will lead to further studies with sharper focus, more certain methodology, and with investigators who will have more adequate time to complete the job. Such a study would be of greater significance if another group receiving drug therapy and psychotherapy was included.

45. Types of Psychotherapy

1. *Listening therapy:* Some analysts (Carl Roger's School) believe that the patients flow of talk should not be interrupted. This may be called the sympathetic ear, and frequently the only feedback is a mild "continue!" or "tut, tut!", or as the old therapist said, "Ach! Who listens!" This is not measurably effective in schizophrenia.

2. *Talking therapy:* Active interchange of a counseling nature between therapist and patient. This is useful, but in the treatment of schizophrenia it must always be of a supportive rather than of a probing nature. It is of secondary importance compared to drug therapy.

3. *Psychoanalysis:* An expensive form of listening and talking therapy which is cultivated and perpetuated by the disciples of Freud, Jung, Adler, and a few later and lesser saints. It is expensive and may continue for years without measurable results. It is not recommended for the schizophrenias.

4. *Group therapy:* At an appointed time a group of patients meet to discuss their problems and seek possible solutions. The similarity of their many problems becomes quickly evident and benefits usually result—depending on the training and ability of

the group leader, who is usually a clinical psychologist, psychiatrist, social worker, or trained counselor, for example, of the ministry.

When the patients congregate on the basis of their disabilities, then the group is called Schizophrenics Anonymous, or Alcoholics Anonymous. The AA group has demonstrated tremendous value over the years.

5. Other types of psychotherapy are useful, but certainly not specific. These are occupational and usually include music, dancing, games, nature walks, work, etc.

Any physician who undertakes to treat a patient must apply recognized and logical procedures. These are:

1. *Diagnosis* of the condition. In mental disease this entails the elimination of brain tumor, psychomotor epilepsy, etc., as the possible cause of the symptoms. A psychometric test such as the MMPI, EWI, or HOD is mandatory. A careful history is essential.

2. *Treatment* by use of the standard therapies, using those drugs with which the doctor has had the greatest experience.

3. *Follow-Up*. In the case of mental patients a program of careful follow-up is necessary to assure continued social rehabilitation.

If the patient has serious mental disease, time is of the essence and should not be squandered by delayed diagnosis, inadequate treatment, or trying the latest fad.

46. Talking Therapy in Schizophrenia

Attempts to treat patients with a serious degree of schizophrenia by means of talking therapy have been dismally unsuccessful. This conclusion is based on the fact that when this approach is adopted, specially trained psychotherapists, who probably have to have a certain kind of personality make-up themselves, are needed; the amount of time and persistence required are forbidding, and the results are dubious.

Conventional psychodynamic formulations explain everything from orifice to anus and can also explain to some degree how the mental functioning of a patient with schizophrenia is altered. Such formulations are also applied to patients who have cancer or other serious illness. But a fundamental difficulty with such formulations is that *they are after the fact and not predictive*. They detail the form of the illness after it has become manifest, but they cannot predict this beforehand and hence are of little value.

Although Sigmund Freud occasionally delved into the histories of schizophrenics to gain further understanding of psychopathology, he was firmly convinced that psychoanalysis is not an appropriate form of treatment for such patients, and he steadfastly refused to accept patients with schizophrenia. He based this on the belief that their disease rendered them incapable of forming the kind of intense emotional relationship (*transference*) with a psychotherapist, which he regarded as essential to a favorable outcome of the treatment.

More recently, Drs. Fromm and Reichmann showed that *transference* could be elicited from a schizophrenic patient, but this required an extraordinary effort in terms of time and dogged refusal to be discouraged. No matter how dedicated the therapist, attempts to treat such patients by these methods may commonly require five or more hours a week for ten or more years. Even then, the improvements may be minimal and can be separated from the natural fluctuations of the illness only with difficulty. Other therapies are more positive and quicker.

There have been variations on the psychoanalytically based approach. One of these was that of Dr. Harry Stack Sullivan, who viewed mental illnesses as "failures in relationships between people" rather than disruptions of processes within people. Time has not shown this to be true, nor can we evolve a successful scheme for the treatment of schizophrenia from this approach.

Dr. Rosen tried another modification which is very close to what Freud called "wild" analysis. Where Freud always insisted that formulations about the patient's thinking and feelings should always be derived from the patient himself without any preconceptions, Dr. Rosen adopted certain interpretations of schizophrenic behavior and ideation as universal and proceeded to batter his patients verbally with these, regardless of their context in terms of the patient's current clinical status. Early remissions were reported, but early remissions are frequent in the so-called "stormy" or "noisy" phase of the illness. This fad has passed with the advent of drug therapy. The foregoing examples are not complete, but have been selected to give representative examples of types of talking therapy which have been tried.

That talking therapy is not an appropriate treatment for schizophrenia is suggested by a study made at the University of Southern California. Here patients were given a combination of talking therapy and medication. Even those who showed the most improvement demonstrated almost no psychological insights relevant to their illness. Nor could it be shown that their degree of improvement was any greater than what might have been expected from medication alone. In another study, a male nurse in an underdeveloped country treated 2,000 male patients with drugs and had the same success rate as that published for modern American mental hospitals, namely, social rehabilitation in about 75 per cent of the patients.

Psychiatry and the patients have suffered in the past from numerous fads because of the lack of any specific treatment for schizophrenia. As medical science has progressed, it is now possible to adhere to specific therapies and treat each disease or symptom on the basis of a rational understanding of its causes and course. Today it is increasingly likely that schizophrenia has a biochemical basis. Talking therapy might in certain cases relieve some of the suffering, as it can for patients with other illnesses. But to expect talking therapy, any more than faith healing, to correct basic organic malfunctioning is, of course, futile. Such a misapplication does an injustice to the method and underestimates the disease.

Some therapists may be likened to the old barnstorming pilot who always flew his airplane by the seat of his pants rather than by modern instruments. This worked well for the pilot on sunny days, but not in clouds or fog. A similar fog is engendered by the two variables, such as adolescence and schizophrenia when they occur together in the teen-ager. Under these circumstances the therapist needs the best and most accurate instruments available. The psychometric tests such as the MMPI, EWI, and HOD card-sort tests are available, can be administered and easily evaluated, and should be used since early drug treatment for the schizophrenic teen-ager is essential to prevent chronic disability.

The teen-ager and the parents should avoid a therapist who is not interested in a differential diagnosis, since an accurate diagnosis alone can lead to adequate therapy. Modern society cannot afford to tolerate the treatment of juvenile schizophrenia by talking therapy alone when better therapy is available.

47. When To Use Talking Therapy

Wise counseling and verbal supportive therapy is useful in the following circumstances:

1. The early adult or teenager may need continuous counsel, because if he has been sick he has missed the maturing effect of the teen-age rat race.

2. The schizophrenic returning to society after several years in a hospital needs counsel. Part of this therapy consists of a constant check on and adjustment of the drug therapy. The patient may

benefit from psychodrama in which he prelives some of the situations he will face in the outer world.

3. Talking therapy of a supportive or reassuring nature may be helpful at any time. Problems of social interaction can be solved or procedures outlined to minimize these problems and thus reduce environmental stress. Hence, talking therapy if expertly directed will help solve the problems of everyday life. If inexpertly directed, talking therapy may dig too deeply and put salt in old wounds, increasing mental stress and the degree of schizophrenia.

4. Talking therapy can bring the patient's attention to his strained relationships with people who are important to him. If he learns to handle these situations better, then mental stress is reduced.

48. The Bewares for Schizophrenics

The schizophrenic, and his loved ones who pay the medical bills should *beware of*:

1. The psychiatrist who states that he doesn't need to use the potent new mental drugs in his practice.

2. The therapist (physician or otherwise) who brags that he will take the personality apart layer by layer and build a new one. (Impossible!)

3. The therapist who says the major tranquilizers are habit forming. Not true!

4. The therapist, who after his talking therapy has failed, states that brain damage must exist.

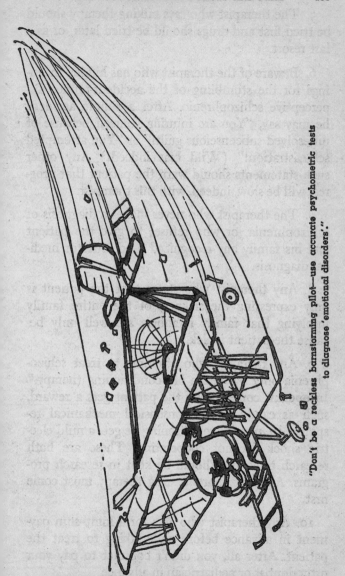

"Don't be a reckless barnstorming pilot—use accurate psychometric tests to diagnose emotional disorders."

5. The therapist who says talking therapy should be tried first and drugs should be tried later, or as a last resort.

6. Beware of the therapist who has hidden meanings for the stumbling of the accident-prone, disperceptive schizophrenic. After a simple accident he may say, "You are injuring yourself because of unresolved subconscious guilt!" or "You attempted self-castration!" (Wild bias indeed!) Any other such statements should warn the patient that progress will be slow, indeed, with this therapist.

7. The therapist who never makes a diagnosis of schizophrenia, or who refuses to give the patient and his family any recognized psychiatric or medical diagnosis.

8. Any therapist who states that the patient is only expressing the sickness of the entire family implying that family members are well only because the patient is sick.

9. Any therapist who attempts to treat schizophrenia only by means of "conditioning therapy." In operant conditioning the patient gets a reward, such as candy, for a nonsensical mechanical response. In *aversive* conditioning he gets a mild electric shock for not cooperating. These are both research tools and should be kept in research programs. Antischizophrenic drug therapy must come first.

10. Any therapist who asks for a lump-sum payment in advance before undertaking to treat the patient. After all, you didn't contract to pay your orthodontist or pediatrician in advance.

11. A therapist who states that hypnotism or dream analysis may provide solid answers in schizophrenia.

12. The therapist who raises the fee and states that you will get more benefit by paying a higher price. An exception occurs when the therapist asks that the patient work and pay the fee rather than the parents. In this case, the patient who earns his way will be more cooperative.

We should perhaps apologize at this point not *to*, but *for*, the professions of psychology and psychiatry. Too many therapists unfortunately believe that they can perform miracles with some *new*(?) technique. If every therapist were required to spend a day in the medical library before starting a *new*(?) technique, his optimism would be sobered. The "bewares" above are based on years of observation of fads in the treatment of schizophrenia. These fads would no longer be proposed if the proposer would only study the documented reports of their inadequacy in schizophrenia.

49. Childhood Schizophrenia and Autism

Halfway Down

Halfway down the stairs
Is a stair
Where I sit.
There isn't any
Other stair
Quite like
it.
I'm not at the bottom,
I'm not at the top;

So this is the stair
Where
I always
Stop.

Halfway up the stairs
Isn't up,
And isn't down.
It isn't in the nursery,
It isn't in the town.
And all sorts of funny thoughts
Run round my head:
"It isn't really
Anywhere!
It's somewhere else
Instead!"

Contrary to some misconceptions, the above delightful verse by A. A. Milne is not evidence of childhood schizophrenia. The child may frequently live in a fantasy-land of imagination and play-acting. Their minds are not yet disciplined by disappointments or inhibited by their elders. Some few students of the mind (who do not know the schizophrenias) have stated that most normal children live in a partial schizophrenic state or pass through schizophrenia as they mature! This fantasy state may occur, but is certainly not schizophrenia.

The schizophrenias, as found in childhood, may be of two types; namely, autism (a self-centered disregard for people combined with repetitive movements) or childhood schizophrenia, which has all or most all of the signs and symptoms seen in the adult or teen-age schizophrenias. These are hallucinations, stereotyped repetitive actions or thoughts, silly grimacing, thought disorders, extreme hyperactivity, and rarely catatonia or waxlike rigidity.

We admire, attempt to preserve, and even long for the active imagination and free wheeling thoughts of the active normal child, but the autistic child is quite the opposite. He is pathetically over-regulated in thought and motor movements. Dr. Bernard Rimland, of San Diego, has likened the autistic child to a traveler on a narrow path, who has the tunnel vision provided by a narrow beam flashlight. The concentration on minute details is enormous, but the assimilation of everyday speech and social interaction is lacking. The idiot savant (a retarded child who can solve large arithmetic problems) may be a subtype of autism.

What is this infantile autism? Dr. Leo Kanner, one of the foremost authorities on the subject, describes it as "children who have been unusual from the beginning of life with withdrawn (autistic) personalities, which cause them always to appear to be living in a private, inaccessible dream world, isolated, seemingly by choice, from contract with others."

Autism can be noticed as early in age as two months, when the child does not respond to friendly overtures. The parents may think the child is just "slow" because he seems dull and uninterested in his surroundings. They may feel the child does not know or recognize them or think of them as any more important than any other person or stranger who comes in contact with him.

The autistic child is usually a handsome, healthy

looking child, but looking into his eyes you discover that the normal sparkle of childhood is missing. He usually does not smile or laugh. He might, however, if he is tickled or involved in a boisterous game of "peek-a-boo." The parents find that all attempts at friendliness or interest on their part is one-sided.

As the child grows to the age of two or more, the parents become more puzzled as to what is really wrong. He has probably mastered too many skills to be considered retarded, and yet he does not seem to be interested in the usual things which interest a two-year-old. He does not care about the names of all the pretty or brightly colored objects shown in his ABC book, but readily learns to point to all the letters or numbers in the book when requested to do so.

Instead of playing with a ball, he may sit on the floor for hours spinning around or simply rocking back and forth. Given a box of blocks, he will sit and throw them all around the room instead of building with them, or he may sit for hours setting one on top of another in a neat row, over and over. He may only like to hammer and sit on the floor hammering on whatever is available for long periods of time.

The autistic child who develops speech uses words primarily to amuse himself instead of to communicate his needs. His speech has a high-pitched sing-songy quality about it. He may readily learn nursery rhymes and little songs on TV commercials and yet be unable to tell you even of an emergency. One three-year-old autistic boy climbed high up on a shelf and was unable to get himself out of that precarious position. He sat there crying until his mother heard him and came to his rescue. Upon seeing his predicament, she tried to get him to verbalize his needs by saying to him, "Say, "Help me! I can't get down!' " In a completely expressionless and rote way he repeated the sentence just as she had spoken it to him. He is usually unable to learn without great difficulty to use "yes" and "no" or speak of himself as "I." One child hurt his hand and came to his mother saying, "Did you hurt yourself?" when he really meant, "I hurt myself."

Just as a deaf child has trouble hearing, so the autistic child has trouble listening as you speak to him. You can literally feel him "tune you out." In the beginning he may only listen to a four-word phrase and then a short simple sentence. He has a tendency to hear only the key words in a sentence, interpreting them in an entirely different way than that meant by the speaker. In all his learning, the autistic child seems able to grasp only the very basic or concrete experiences of life, but is unable to add to his basics the abstract concepts of human experience and learning.

Dr. Rimland defines this as follows: "The child with early infantile autism is grossly impaired in a function basic to all cognition, the ability to relate new stimuli to remembered experience." This crippling learning disability manifests itself in every area of his existence. He can learn words that he can "see" happening. Example: "The red ball is rolling off the table" is said to him as the speaker rolls the ball off the edge of the table.

The child may readily learn to read the primer used in a first grade reading class, since it is very concrete and basic; but as he progresses to the second and third grade level where reading contains abstract concepts, he will learn to read the words, but not understand their meaning. As he grows older, the autistic child, because of his inability to build on to his primary social experiences, seems to function socially and emotionally at a much lower level than he does intellectually.

Until very recently, childhood autism was thought by many authorities on the subject to be caused by a faulty environment, mainly an impaired mother-child relationship. It was determined that the child seemed cold and aloof, because his mother did not pick him up and relate to him in a warm, affectionate way. Some authorities describe parents of autistic children as being generally "loners," quiet, unsociable, rather withdrawn people. To our knowledge, this generalization is completely false. The parents of autistic children who are known to the writer are generally warm, outgoing, and responsive people. Most of them have several other normal children. More up-to-date thinking and information seems to indicate that autism may result from a rare recessive inherited trait, or be otherwise determined by biological factors. Along these lines, some authorities feel it is caused by an imbalance in body chemistry. Others feel it is some form of undetermined brain damage. We refer to the autistic child as "he" since the disorder is four times more frequent in the male than in the female.

Will talking therapy or play therapy cure the child? To date, there has not been one known instance of a child cured of autism by talking therapy. However, the therapist can sometimes be of great help in bringing out the child's full, but limited, potential. The therapist can as a friend, through play therapy, help the child to relate to someone in authority other than his parents. One autistic child had such an excellent relationship with his therapist that he was able to carry this over to any camp counselor, teacher, or doctor who worked with him.

Since all parents have a deep emotional investment in their children, it is sometimes very difficult for them to accept or even cope with their autistic child. If the parent is an emotionally well-adjusted person, who feels at ease and comfortable in his life relationships, he can make a much better adjustment. On the other hand, if a parent has many feelings of inadequacy about himself and has been unable to make a satisfactory adjustment to life's problems, he may have a difficult time, and he may also project these feelings on the child. A good and sympathetic therapist can be of great help in working with the parent to sift through his feelings and attitudes of guilt, sorrow, and inadequacy—since with autism we are all inadequate.

The danger in the whole picture in talking therapy for both the therapist and the parent is that either or both may lose sight of their goal which is to *help to improve the behavior of the child*. The autistic child will, just as any normal child, function and develop better in a non-hostile environment. He needs a good home and good school setting to bring out his best potential within the framework of his disability.

At present, a great deal of research is being done biochemically. There is some indication that large doses of pyridoxine, niacinamide, and vitamin C may help in some cases. There have been isolated cases of help by several other drugs, such as Deaner and the antipsychotic drugs, but, as a whole, specific chemotherapy research is in its infancy. Deaner, and even the first dose of a drug such as Thorazine, may appear to make the child worse. Each drug should be tried alone and for at least two weeks before discontinuation of the drug trial. During this two-week period the dose of the drug under test should be regulated up or down, according to its effect. Since the children are overstimulated, caffeine and the amphetamines should be avoided.

These young patients cooperate well in a biologically oriented research program. They usually allow blood to be taken, perhaps protesting "don't hurt," but at the same time showing no painful reaction to the needle. Some biological research studies are in progress, and therein lies the real hope for the treatment of autism and childhood schizophrenia.

Schizophrenia is difficult to diagnose in the first ten years of life. In fact, several decades ago it was believed that schizophrenia did not occur at all under the age of ten. We now know it occurs and can even be diagnosed at the age of several months. Where the incidence of childhood schizophrenia in some countries or regions is reported to be extremely low, it may be assumed that this is the result of inaccurate statistics, because the illness was not recognized. In such cases, the children are called behavioral problems or emotionally disturbed or are considered to be mentally retarded. Confusing schizophrenia with retardation in the young is due to the habit of diagnosing symptoms instead of the disease. A most critical period occurs in human beings when they learn to speak. If for any reason, they are unable to learn during this period, they may not learn at all. If schizophrenia occurs under the age of ten, it may interfere with the learning process, and the child's learning may be permanently impaired. Diagnosis under the age of ten is most difficult, since such a child is not testable by such adjuncts as psychiatric history or the HOD and the Experiential World Inventory tests. However, the Mauve Factor Test on the urine and the electroencephalographic studies on the brain are most valuable when these can be done. During maturity, schizophrenia is most readily diagnosed, for at this period of life personality has more or less stabilized, and even subtle changes in personality can be determined more readily. This is not true for the child under ten, since we cannot distinguish a clear personality change, but parents and teachers note failing school grades or an inability to keep up with others of his age. Alteration in personality is the one important, unchanging characteristic of the disease, and in order to evaluate the change we must know the personality before the change. This is obtained from the teachers and parents. Objective tests, such as the handwriting and drawings by the patient prior to his illness, are most valuable.

Childhood is the period in life when schizophrenia can do the most harm. The earlier the onset of the disorder, the more grave the consequences, unless the illness disappears spontaneously or as a result of early treatment. The illness will have the most damaging effects if it comes on either before, or shortly after, speech has fully developed. One of the serious effects of the disease developing at this time is that vocalization stops Young children who have learned a few words seem unable to learn more and often forget the ones they have already learned. If the disease recedes, the degree to which speech will recover depends on the duration of the illness.

Schizophrenic children have many of their senses altered. The world of the schizophrenic child is not at all like ours. He may suffer distortions in perception of time, space, seeing, hearing, and of his own body. The intense hyperactivity so characteristic of the very young schizophrenic child may be the result of his distorted way of experiencing time —perhaps a speeding up produced by brain stimulation. The repetitive questioning seen in almost all schizophrenic children may likewise be due to this anomaly in time perception. Even though only seconds or minutes may have passed, the child may experience the brief interval, like the passage of many hours without his question having been answered.

The distortions in spatial relationships frequently produces deviant ways of walking. The child may walk in a zig-zag pattern or with his legs high, wide, and handsome. Usually he is clumsy and will bump into furniture. He may exhibit poor balance and fall frequently. If it is not understood that a child's perceptions are distorted in schizophrenia and the symptoms interpreted, the child may be wrongly diagnosed as suffering from organic brain disease. One might challenge any child psychiatrist or neurologist making such a diagnosis to walk properly without stumbling and falling if he found the floor to be rocking back and forth, up and down, and tilting at alarming angles, while his depth perception was also faulty.

The schizophrenic child appears to be disoriented, confused and anxious and often expresses deep concern about his relationship with his environment. He often realizes that he is confused. One young patient, age 12, prior to treatment exhibited uncontrollable hyperactivity, restlessness, and impulsivity. He seemed to be continually in motion regardless of circumstances and was introspectively aware of the explosively uncontrolled nature of his disturbance, about which he complained at times with an air of bewilderment, usually with threats of dire consequences to his parents or to the therapist if they did not help him at once in overcoming the intolerable suffering. There is no joy in schizophrenia even in childhood.

Studies indicate that the schizophrenic child has a deviant pattern of receptor preferences in which the distance receptors of vision and audition are avoided, and the child engages with the world through the proximal receptors of touch, taste, and smell. He may, therefore, have trouble recognizing people and even his parents. When his hearing is distorted and disturbed he may be unable to localize sources of sounds and may, therefore, pay no attention to sounds. He is most often hypersensitive to sounds, yet at times so hyposensitive as to make no response to loud sounds. The absence of response frequently leads to the suspicion that the child is deaf. One mother reported that her child behaved at times in such a manner as to indicate that he could hear, yet frequently behaved as though he was deaf. To test his hearing, she would occasionally come up behind him carrying a pot cover in each hand and, using them like cymbals, would crash them together either above or behind his head. The child would make no sign of recognition.

One of the major symptoms of schizophrenic illness in children is hyperactivity which may range from persistent restlessness to constant and almost total body movements, body rocking, and head banging. The mother of one patient reported that he developed well until three years of age when his illness began. Until age six, his hyperactivity was so marked that he was able to sleep but one hour out of every 24. Niacinamide and vitamin C then controlled his symptoms.

While the schizophrenic child can be engaged and involved he is usually inattentive and is incapable of sustained effort. He also exhibits a diminution or absence of pain response to physical traumata, which in normal children usually elicit pain and crying.

The following case illustrates that hallucinatory experiences can frequently be clearly elicited in schizophrenic children. Steven is a six and one-half-year-old, who sat restlessly but patiently in the chair in the doctor's office. When asked why his mother brought him, he quietly answered, "Because I have nightmares and daymares." He told his mother that pictures on the wall looked real, that he was afraid to stay alone in the room at home where his grandfather's picture hung, because he always looked as though he were moving. At times he told his mother that she looked small and "flat," while pictures looked like real people. Whenever he had a cold or a virus infection his perceptional abnormalities became worse. During a recent illness, he said that he felt like a stuffed toy. Steven's illness manifested itself frankly at age three with great hyperactivity and aimless running. He also responded to niacinamide and vitamin C therapy.

The response to the nicotinic acid treatment is slow and three to six months is the minimum time for the maximal significant changes to become manifest. Most parents have reported that the first noticeable change is a slowing of the hyperactivity. Attendant on this slowing is a willingness to learn.

For information about brain injured children contact:

> New Jersey Association for Brain Injured
> Children
> 61 Lincoln Street
> East Orange, New Jersey
> 201-675-0112

50. The Economics of Schizophrenia

There is no question as to whether or not this illness is *expensive. It is!* The major question is, "How expensive?" While no survey of charges is known, some personal experience with charges for hospitals, doctors, medication, special treatment, travel, and other items may provide useful guides as to what to expect. These costs were incurred during 1963–1967 and need adjustment upward to reflect current prices.

Hospitals:

In general, hospitals, with teaching, training, and research facilities, are the most expensive. They have costs running from $50 to $70 per day. These high costs are, in part, due to the high cost of personnel. These hospitals tend to have the highest number of nurses, attendants, specialists, and doctors per patient.

There are also special purpose clinics catering to mental illness. These have both in- and out-patient service. They are designed to provide quick, restorative treatment. In two of these we have experienced rates of about $40 per day with medication. Doctors' fees and charges for electric shock therapy (EST) or other special treatment may be extra.

Least expensive, but also least able to provide attention to the patient, are the state hospitals. These are free to state residents in New Jersey if the family income is low. When charges are billed to those who can pay, the rates have been about ten dollars per day. This charge includes everything. Parenthetically, a state hospital is no place to take good clothes or personal belongings—clothes and other belongings may be lost or stolen.

Also, it is worth noting that if patients are allowed home for week-ends or brief stays, there is no charge for such days.

Hospital costs depend greatly on the length of stay. When the patient is ill enough to require state hospitalization, then a lengthy stay in this secure and different environment is needed for the patient to recover sufficiently to return to a more normal society. This stay is seldom less than one month, but, can extend into many months or even years.

In northern New Jersey, many county hospitals are better than the state hospitals. The war veteran should make arrangements to receive the excellent care provided in the Veterans Hospitals. A similar system exists for merchant seamen.

Doctors:

When the patient is not in a hospital he will have doctors' fees. In our experience, psychiatrists' costs have varied from $25 to $40 per hour visit. We have found doctors willing to discuss charges if they felt the costs were so burdensome that the patient might be unwilling to keep up recommended treatment. As in hospitals, the costs are a matter of time and frequency of visits. Psychiatrists have suggested twice a month or even longer intervals. The length of time under the doctor's care varies to some degree with the approach of the doctor, the nature of the illness, and the doctor's busy schedule. Doctors seeking to discover causes and those who use psychotherapy or analysis require the longest treatment time.

Somewhat lesser fees are charged by psychologists. These have been about $20 to $30 per hour with something less for group therapy sessions. As in the case of psychiatrists, there is sympathetic concern for the family's ability to pay.

Travel:

All of these forms of treatment require travel. Travel costs can mount up if visiting is maintained during hospitalization. Arrangements for baby-sitters or home care also may be required. Expenses of this sort are not eligible for reimbursement under most hospitalization or "major medical" policies.

(It can, however, be claimed as a medical expense on your income tax.)

Special treatment:

Special treatments for an in-patient are often extra cost items. Electric shock therapy and insulin coma therapy have varied from as little as ten dollars per treatment for in-patients to as much as $40 per treatment for outside maintenance shock treatments. In state hospitals these costs are not extra, but the treatments are often more widely spaced and thus require longer periods of hospitalization. Special tests and group therapy are additional items that may be free in hospitals, but will require special charges if they are necessary for an out-patient.

Medication:

The antipsychotic drugs can be expensive. One family we know spent $350 on drugs. Some prescriptions have cost as much as 50 to 70 cents per tablet, and dosages can be as much as six tablets per day, or three to four dollars per day. It is refreshing to note that niacinamide and vitamin C tablets can be purchased directly, so that a 3.0 gram per day dosage of each can be as little as 20 cents a day.

Insurance:

Insurance can help to pay for many of these costs. Under Blue Cross contracts, we have found that the patient is eligible for 20 to 30 days' hospitalization in one contract year. This certainly helps, but seldom can a hospitalization be completed within this period. Many employers provide major medical insurance for further protection.

This covers medical costs not covered under Blue Cross or other hospitalization insurance. While they certainly help, most of these contracts have limits. These are usually total dollar and time limits. Virtually all of these require an initial payment by the insured—from $50 to $500, plus a percentage payment of all subsequent costs.

Those patients who have paid into Social Security should investigate the possibility of permanent or temporary disability payments. Under the 1965 Law, any insured worker whose disability is expected to last at least 12 months may qualify for disability benefits at the beginning of the seventh month. Chronic schizophrenia qualifies as a disability.

Other costs:

There are special problems and costs if the patient is the breadwinner. He may have some limited sick leave, but this is seldom enough to cover the period of hospitalization. At this point the question of family income becomes an overpowering problem. If the ill person is the mother, then similar real and big problems of home maintenance and housekeeping arise.

Besides hospitals there are other types of "away from home" living arrangements—camps, halfway houses, and other possibilities. Halfway houses provided by the state are considered extensions of the hospitals, and the rates are the same. We have also investigated social camps and have been quoted rates of as much as $600 per month. For children there are also special schools. For comparative purposes, two such schools (one in Pennsylvania and the other in Connecticut) quoted in 1967 a cost of $10,000 per year. The Pennsylvania school would not break down this expense into medical vs. educational costs. In 1969, one school quotes $18,000 for 12 months.

If a community mental health center is nearby, the patient can frequently be treated at home after the diagnosis is established. For this purpose the visiting nurse is extremely valuable. The public health nurse may also be able to give relatives valuable advice in regard to local treatment facilities.

In New Jersey, under the Beadleson Act, the home-bound patient is entitled to continued schooling. This must be asked for and, frequently, insisted on by the parent. This service is obtained by application through the local school board. This office may also arrange for training in a vocational school.

Finally, do not overlook the New Jersey Rehabilitation Commission, Room 307 Raymond Boulevard, Newark, New Jersey, 07102. This office may evaluate the degree of disability under Social Security. This may be a valuable financial aid when the head of the family is ill.

51. How About Me and Thee and our Schizophrenias?

If we consult the books on psychology or psychiatry we find two difficulties: one is that many signs of schizophrenia are described without distinguishing how these are different, if at all, from the same signs in normal people. The other is that great disagreements exist among psychiatrists about the significance of the clinical features. The critical reader of these books usually ends up with real doubt as to just how schizophrenia can be recognized in patients, let alone in me and thee!

For example, the schizophrenic has disperceptions and hallucinations, but *we also* may have mild hallucinations when disperception overtakes us while driving a car at dusk before our eyes are dark-adapted or, even worse, while driving in a fog or snowstorm when visibility is impaired. This disperception can produce illusions and hallucinations which are most uncomfortable and dangerous. This may be similar to sensory isolation, which is known to produce hallucinations. Also the sleep-deprived subject, after two or three days, starts hallucinating and may become very paranoid. Paranoia may occur even in the normal individual when sleep-deprived.

For example, one common claim is that schizophrenic patients suffer from a "disorder of thinking." While this is often invoked in making the diagnosis, the exact definition is hazy since the disorder may involve only abstract thinking on a single subject matter, such as radio waves or the police. Moreover, to us and the patient, a disorder of thinking may vary with the time of day, since we know that, on awakening, our thoughts may be disordered. Some people think more clearly in the morning, while others are mentally more alert in the late hours of the evening.

What aspects of schizophrenia are easy to recognize and important to the relatives? In other words, what are the manifestations which distinguish the illness, so that people without technical training can distinguish it from other disturbances? There are several telltale areas in which untreated schizophrenics have difficulty which can be recognized easily. One is their inability to adjust to different circumstances.

In dealing with changing circumstances, we can always be most effective if we have at our command a diversity of ways of acting and reacting. In addition, we need mobility in switching from one approach to another so that we can adopt the most effective way quickly. While doing this, we must be able to weigh each solution in turn to see if it will work, or whether another should be used. This testing and learning process provides diversity and mobility to our thoughts and acts. The *untreated* schizophrenic lacks this elasticity altogether. He may only deal in rigid stereotypes, and he behaves the same regardless of how inappropriate or maladaptive his action becomes. He does not modify or learn from experience. How well or how badly he gets along in life depends on (1) how severe the incongruity becomes between this stereotyped behavior and the real circumstances, and (2) how well the drugs and somatic therapies restore this normal process. This abnormal process cannot be modified by talking therapy.

Secondly, the untreated schizophrenic acts *as if* he is entirely selfish and unable to love or even be fond of a dog, let alone a human being! The mark of a sound and mature personality is caring for other people, being able to love others. The normal person growing up comes to recognize his own mortality and imperfection. One real solution to the stress and the other trials of life is the formation of intense emotional relationships usually with ones family or friends, in which one comes to care as much for others as one's self. This brings enrichment of life with warmth, closeness, and mutual good deeds, which can be achieved in no other way. Like other mental patients, but to a far more severe and intractable degree, the untreated schizophrenic is hampered in his capacity for forming such close relationships. If untreated he may live entirely alone on his little island of self absorption or grandiosity. Attempts to elicit feelings of friendship are met with indifference, contempt, or hostility. Dealings with others are strictly on an even exchange basis, oftentimes more or less bizarre in nature. While other mental patients also are often like this, they are not so completely rigid.

Once the talking therapist gets past the defensive fears of the schizophrenic the intensity of the available feeling and loyalty of the patient can be overwhelming. The therapist must be utterly honest and unafraid. The patient demands more naked honesty than some guarded therapists can give. If the therapist cannot be utterly honest, the patient will remain cold and withdrawn. The schizophrenic, when he considers it safe, is usually too frank and loving.

Humor combines these two aspects of human living. Humor requires complex and rapid rearrangements of ideas, which is a difficult process for the fixedly rigid mental processes of the untreated schizophrenic. In addition, humor basically concerns people and their interactions with each other. In this respect, it often serves as a useful safety valve for tensions. The ability to laugh off things that are distressing and yet cannot be changed is also completely absent in the untreated schizophrenic. These patients are likely to perceive humor as insulting, and instead of smiling, they react like Tam O'Shanter's wife: "Gathering her brow like gathering a storm, nursing her wrath to keep it warm."

Normal appreciation of humor returns with treatment. For example, a paranoid schizophrenic on the mend related to us how jealous he was of his wife. When he was on the 4:00 p.m. shift he called home frequently to try to catch her out—which would mean with another man, of course. We made him laugh at himself when he realized that he never called home when he was on the 8:00 a.m. to 4:00 p.m. shift. He really laughed at the fact that he was suspicious of his wife only when he worked on the evening shift, but, if unfaithful, she had the same eight hours to cheat in the morning as in the evening.

Thirdly we would like to re-emphasize that the schizophrenic suffers from a distortion of the world about him, which is called disperception. This is like looking in a shattered or distorted mirror in a house of horrors. The disperception may involve all of his five senses, his sense of time, the size of his body, and his perception of those around him. These distortions may occupy his mind and give rise to inappropriate grimaces. His personal space may be distorted so that he talks to you with his head only 12 inches away instead of the usual more comfortable two to three feet. Some of these disperceptions are measured accurately in the HOD and EWI tests for schizophrenia.

Finally, as we have previously noted, the schizophrenic is frequently overstimulated perhaps from some chemical in his body. This results in insomnia, fatigue, and restlessness.

Thus, schizophrenia can be recognized by these four signs (1) stereotyped behavior, (2) the ability to make enemies rather than friends, (3) the various disperceptions which alter behavior, and (4) the overstimulation which may be so severe as to turn day into night and night into nightmares.

How about thee then? Looking at yourself what do you find? Do any or all of these four marks of schizophrenia operate so strongly as to interfere with your normal day-to-day living? Are you one of the walking wounded, the nonhospitalized two per cent who might benefit by modern day treatment? As you ask yourself, so I will ask myself, I hope that for both of us these signs are not present, but if they are we now know what to do about them.

52. Books for Further Reading

The average layman involved in schizophrenia, because of self interest or the illness of a relative, will only pursue reading matter that pertains to his immediate interest. Therefore, if the relative is hospitalized, he is more interested in the new media that may tell of new advances. Such a reliable magazine is the *Journal of Schizophrenia*, the only scientific periodical devoted entirely to schizophrenia. This is available with a participating membership in the American Schizophrenia Foundation. Other important articles may appear in the *Journal of Nervous and Mental Diseases, Biological Psychiatry*, and the *International Journal of Neuropsy-*

chiatry. The British Journal of Psychiatry and *Nature* have articles frequently on the biology of schizophrenia.

For background reading, four books are recommended:

1. "How to Live with Schizophrenia," by Abram Hoffer, M.D., and Humphry Osmond, M.R.C.P.—$5.95

2. "In Search of Sanity—The Journal of a Schizophrenic," by Gregory Stefan— $5.00

The above are published by University Books, Inc., New Hyde Park, New York 11401.

3. "A Mind That Found Itself," by Clifford Beer (Written more than 50 years ago).

4. *Effects of Psychotherapy,* by Hans J. Eysenck. This book argues that psychotherapeutic treatment, whether Freudian or otherwise, has never been known to give better results than those obtained without such treatment. Seventeen prominent psychoanalysts and psychologists discuss his contention. Price—$6.50

The U.S. Veterans Administration has a medical bulletin MB-11 (1966) on "Medication and Tranquilizers" which sells for 20 cents. Superintendent of Documents, U.S. Printing Office, Washington, D.C. 20402

"Public Affairs Publications" have pamphlets at 50 cents each.

During the recovery period of the patient, there is considerable reading matter available from the organization of Recovery, Incorporated, 116 South Michigan Ave., Chicago, Illinois 60603. Members of this organization meet regularly, every day of the week in every state of the Union. Books written by Dr. Abraham Low, founder of the group, give specific directions toward rehabilitation.

The National Association for Mental Health has a magazine for $2 per year which is issued every three months (quarterly). The National Commission on Mental Illness publishes books on Community Programs, and the American Psychological Association, 1200-17th Street, Washington, D.C. has material for the layman.

Finally, a new book by Louise Wilson, entitled "This Stranger, My Son," details the haunting anguish and rising expenses which grip a family when a child has untreated chronic paranoid schizophrenia. Specific therapy is not mentioned in the book. (G. P. Putnam—$4.95)

ADDENDUM

The members of the Schizophrenia Foundation of New Jersey deeply appreciate the efforts of our Professional Committee that made this primer possible. Not only has it given us a more knowledgeable understanding of this strange illness, but comforts us in the thought that it will bring help to countless others whose lives have also been burdened by schizophrenia. Only those who have seen a loved one in the grip of this variegated and devastating illness can understand the profound sadness it incurs. This primer has changed our despair to hope and for this we are grateful.

ACKNOWLEDGMENT

From the book WHEN WE WERE VERY YOUNG by A.A. Milne. Copyright, 1924, by E.P. Dutton & Co., Inc. Renewal, 1952, by A.A. Milne. Reprinted by permission of the publisher.